GPST STAGE 3

SELECTION CENTRE

Ultimate Guide to the GPST/GPVTS Selection Centre

Gail Allsopp

4th edition

Published by: ISC Medical, 97 Judd Street, London WC1H 9JG
www.iscmedical.co.uk - Tel: 0845 226 9487

First Edition: October 2007
2nd Edition: October 2008
3rd Edition: October 2009
This Edition: November 2011

ISBN13: 978-1-905812-23-3
A catalogue record for this book is available from the British Library.

The author has, as far as possible, taken care to ensure that the information given in this text is accurate and up to date. However, readers are strongly advised to confirm that the information with regards to specific patient management complies with current legislation, guidelines and local protocols.

The information within this text is intended as a study aid for the purpose of the GPST/GPVTS selection examinations. It is not intended, nor should it be used as a medical reference for the direct management of patients or their conditions.

The names, cases and situations in this book are all fictitious. Any similarity to real life is a coincidence.

Contents

Introduction

Welcome to the 4th edition of our popular guide to the GPST/GPVTS assessment centre and congratulations to those who have bought this book in preparation for the Stage 3 assessment centre after successfully completing the Stage 2 examination for General Practice training. You are now over halfway through the selection process and getting ever closer to securing the most wonderful job in the world.

If you are reading this prior to Stage 2, good luck with the exam. You will find that some of the ethical information in this book may be relevant to the Stage 2 assessment. However, most of the Stage 2 questions are clinically based, and I would therefore suggest that you concentrate on passing Stage 2 before embarking on reading the rest of this book.

There is always a great deal of anxiety surrounding the General Practice Specialist Training (GPST) application process. Be assured that the GP assessment and selection process is very robust, fair, extensively tried and tested and most importantly of all, designed to appoint the best candidates.

Don't panic; and don't allow yourself to become caught up in the frenzy of the process. Be confident in your own ability and be assured that you can secure that training post by understanding the process, identifying your own strengths and weaknesses, confirming your strengths and working to improve those weaknesses by completing adequate preparation.

By the end of the book, you will feel much better informed with regard to what to expect during your assessment, and more prepared to face the tasks presented to you on the day. I hope to enhance your knowledge and give you examples that allow you to practise in a safe environment at home, which, in turn, should make you more confident during your assessment.

This book cannot replace practice and face-to-face feedback by others. Therefore, if you can do so, use the examples provided in this book to practise with friends and colleagues. Find someone you trust to give you honest and constructive feedback to allow you to improve.

I would highly recommend attending a formal course. Choose your course by recommendation. Find one with a small number of candidates that aims to give individual feedback related to your performance in the practical challenges you will face during your assessment. Look at who is teaching on the course. Are they GPs? Are they trained? Do they have experience of the application process?

If you do decide to attend a course, be honest with yourself and listen to the feedback given. It is very unlikely that the feedback you receive from a formally trained course tutor is inaccurate. Remember that they are trying to help you improve. They have nothing to gain from lying to you. If you are given feedback that you do not agree with, reflect on it for a while. Could it be true? I have lost count of the number of candidates who arrive at a course stating that one of their strengths is communication and, when it comes to showing those skills in a practical station such as role play, cannot accept any hints and tips on how to improve. If you believe you are the best at something, you may be right, but everyone has the capacity to improve. Why not aim to be even better? Choose a course that will give you the individual attention to achieve that.

Good luck!

Gail

B About the author

I have been where you are now. I have first-hand experience of the selection process and understand how you are feeling now in the run-up to the Stage 3 assessment. This insight, in addition to the following experience, puts me in a unique position to write this book. I hope you find it useful.

My experience includes:

- Working as a partner in General Practice

- 14 years of clinical medical practice

- 18 years' experience of teaching others

- Formal training in all aspects of communication from non-verbal to specific verbal communication

- Professionally trained actress

- Work as an actor patient for medical examinations

- The use of role play and forum theatre to teach a variety of professionals (including civil servants, lawyers and medical personnel)

- Running one-day Stage 2 / Stage 3 courses for GPST applicants for ISC Medical

C   The assessment

The Stage 3 assessment for General Practice is undertaken at a selection centre. The selection process has evolved over the years and now involves an assessment using 2 separate styles of stations. Each station is run and assessed independently and the marking (as with all assessments for jobs) is based on the personal specification provided; therefore ensure that you have downloaded a copy of the person specification from the official GP recruitment website (www.gprecruitment.org.uk) and that you know it inside out and back to front!

The stations are as follows:

Station 1: **Role play / Simulated consultations and meetings**
Three scenarios lasting 10 minutes each (30 minutes in total):

- One scenario with a patient
- One scenario with a relative or carer
- One scenario with a colleague

Station 2: **Prioritisation task**
A written exam lasting 30 minutes

Both stations and their common variations will be discussed at length in the following chapters. They can be assessed in any order on the day so follow any instructions given to you closely. Ensure that you read all the official information sent to you (usually by email). Things change, so check your email daily and check your junk mail every day – it would be a shame to miss the selection process for email-related technical issues.

Setup and practical advice

Timing

In total the assessment lasts 1 hour (30 minutes for the written exercise and 30 minutes for the role play/simulation exercises, which consists of 3 scenarios each lasting 10 minutes).

Due to organisational factors, you will need to be at the selection centre for longer than that. In some places, your actual presence time may exceed 3 hours. Read all the information sent to you to ensure that you know what will happen at the centre which you have been invited to attend.

Punctuality

Ensure that you turn up on-time. If the centre is in an area that you don't know well, plan your route in advance. Try the route beforehand so you know how long it will take you. Allow some extra time for unexpected delays. It sounds obvious, but how many times have you seen candidates rushing in at the last minute, out of breath and stressed? Don't let this be you. Your chance of getting a job rests on this one assessment. Why risk it?

Organisation

The selection centres run to a tight timetable. In addition to arriving on time, it is important that you know where you need to be, and at what time, within your centre. When you arrive, you may be given a paper copy of a timetable; or it may be on a board or overhead projector (OHP) as you enter. Make a note of your candidate number and work out which room you should be in and at what time each station will start. Be punctual. Be prepared. Take with you a pen and some paper to write down the timetable just in case you are not given a hard copy of it.

What will happen on the day?

After signing in, you will likely be given a candidate number and asked to wear this on a badge or sticker for the duration of the assessment. Many centres then take your photograph to ensure that the correct person is attending each part of the assessment. There will then be a waiting area for all the candidates to gather in prior to the start of the assessment.

What should you wear?

Read the information sent to you. Most selection centres state that you should be smart, but casual. What does that mean? Be comfortable, but remember that you are being assessed for a professional job and that one of the assessments is with a simulated patient. You need to look presentable enough to meet a "patient" (who may be a traditional older patient), but comfortable enough to sit for 2-3 hours. Some people wear suits but many are dressed in their usual (possibly best) work clothes. If you are buying something new, try it on and wear it at home for a few hours. You need to ensure that nothing disrupts your concentration for the time that you are there. The tight shirt, hot or itchy jacket, skirt that needs pulling down or top that rides up to show your midriff are all distractions that are easily avoided.

Ladies, it doesn't matter if you wear a skirt, dress or trousers as long as it fits the above criteria. Be comfortable and professional.

As an actor, I never feel fully in character until I put on the shoes to complete the costume. It is the same for me in interviews. Think about your footwear. Make sure your shoes are comfortable. If they are new, wear them for a while at home. Avoid the distracting blister that is bound to happen on the way to the selection centre. If they are old, make sure that they are cleaned. There may not be an explicit mark for the way you dress but it will make you look more credible and professional; it will also give you that added bit of confidence you need to spur you on.

Attitude

You are unlikely to be marked for the way in which you behave outside of the structured assessed tasks, but in theory there is someone watching you from the minute you enter the selection centre until the time that you leave. Think about the way in which you wish to be perceived. It does not mean that you should take on a character as you enter the building; one of the strengths of the assessment centre is that it assesses each candidate over a long period of time and so, unless you are a fabulous actor, it is unlikely that you will be able to maintain a false personality over a prolonged period of time. Instead, be yourself, but show the side of your personality that you want others to see. The staff who greet you and formally sign you in deserve as much respect as the patient whom you will meet in the role play / simulated consultation station. The other candidates are competitors, but they are also your colleagues and, as you will see later, your interaction with colleagues will be formally assessed within the role play station of the assessment centre.

Official documentation to take with you

Again, read the information sent to you by your individual selection centre and follow those guidelines. They often ask for the original and a photocopy of a number of official papers. If a copy is requested, ensure that you take it along. They will keep the photocopy once they have checked it alongside the original.

Avoid leaving any original document behind. It is very common for these to go missing. If it is essential that you leave an original document, ensure you have a photocopy at home and get a receipt from the member of staff who is taking it away. This way, if the original is not returned to you, you have proof that it was handed over to an official. Ensure that you take their name so that you can claim any reimbursement required for originals to be replaced.

The evidence commonly expected includes:

1 – Photographic identification
This is required to prove you are who you say you are. Your NHS card or passport is normally sufficient.

2 – Driving licence

One of the eligibility criteria for entry into General Practice training is that you have a valid driving licence or can demonstrate that you can fulfil the requirements of the post (e.g. providing emergency care, home visits). You may be forgiven for thinking that, since most of you will start training in a hospital, you do not need a driving licence straight away; however, many GPST rotations will have an ITP (Innovative Training Post) in the first two years, which will mean working in General Practice before year three. If you do not have a valid driving licence, do not panic. Write a letter stating that you are willing to provide your own transport when required. This may mean paying for taxis or purchasing a bicycle while learning to drive, but this declaration will be enough to satisfy the entry criteria.

3 – Evidence of qualifications

Your primary medical qualification (translated into English if not originally in English) and any postgraduate examinations certificates that you have attained.

4 – Evidence of competencies

Foundation doctors will need to take along their signed certificate stating that they have achieved Foundation level competencies within the last 3 years. If you have not achieved year 2 competencies, get a letter from your current educational supervisor stating that they expect you to have achieved the required competencies by the end of your F2 (Foundation two) year. If you have not completed the standard foundation years training then there is an Alternative Certificate that can be submitted (See http://www.gprecruitment.org.uk).

5 – GMC registration

A copy of your current licence to practice.

6 – English language proficiency

If your original medical degree was not taught in English, proof of your proficiency in English will be required.

8 – Portfolio and CV

Currently, there is no requirement to take along your CV and portfolio (many of which will be internet-based in the future) to your assessment centre, unless your individual centre requests to see it. You may not receive the information from the selection centre until a few days before you go, so it is good practice to have an up-to-date CV and ensure that your portfolio is completed well in advance of the Stage 3 assessment. Specialities other than General Practice often have a section of their interview dedicated to reviewing the candidates' portfolio. This is not the case currently with General Practice, but, as ever, things change, so be prepared for every eventuality.

Job selection

You are often asked to rank the available rotations within your deanery at the selection centre. Some deaneries will give you the information in advance by post or email and give you time at home to think about your preferences for where you would like to work. Others present you with a list of regions or individual rotations when you arrive for you to rank in order of preference. Make sure you have thought about this before you go. Go onto the deanery website and look through the rotations. Think about the geography and, if you don't know the area, buy and take along a map to your assessment. Don't be caught out or risk the added pressure by being presented with this on the day. A couple of hours of advance planning go a long, long way.

Additional tasks

Some deaneries will give you an introductory talk at the beginning of your selection centre to explain the process. Many will have a question and answer section at some point during the session.

The final request at the selection centre is usually for feedback if this has not been covered in a question and answer session or "unmarked, structured interview". Those organising the selection centre take the feedback you give seriously and your comments will shape the selection centres of the future. Please spend a little time giving honest feedback. Your voice and opinion are important.

Assessment criteria

Having completed the Stage 1 eligibility application form and passed the Stage 2 exam-based assessment, it is now assumed that you have the necessary clinical knowledge and that you fulfil the criteria required to achieve a place on a GP training scheme. Stage 3 is a way of choosing the best candidates by assessing the core competencies and shortlisting criteria agreed nationally. You need to be "safe" clinically, but the selection centre is not all about clinical knowledge. As you will see it is about much, much more...

GPST Person Specification

The National Person Specification for General Practice training is published by the National Recruitment Office for General Practice Training (www.gprecruitment.org.uk).

The main competencies that will be tested at the selection centre include:

- Empathy & Sensitivity
- Communication Skills
- Conceptual Thinking & Problem Solving
- Coping with Pressure
- Organisation & Planning
- Managing Others & Team Involvement
- Professional Integrity
- Learning & Personal Development
- Clinical knowledge and expertise
- Language skills (both verbal and non verbal)

Read carefully through the specification, digest it and appreciate the qualities that the assessors will be looking for. Each of the tasks will be testing several of the core competencies.

The basic principles of each of the core competencies are also explained in detail in the General Medical Council (GMC) publication entitled *Good Medical Practice (2006)*. Make sure that you read your booklet attentively. If it has been accidentally filed in the bin, you can find it on the GMC website (www.gmc-uk.org)

Example of competencies assessed by task

Role play / Simulation exercise
This will clearly test your communication skills, your empathy and sensitivity, problem solving, organisation and planning and, to a small extent, your clinical knowledge base. Depending on the scenario, the interaction with a colleague will also test your professional integrity, ability to work with colleagues, probity and your ability to cope with pressure.

Prioritisation exercise
This is definitely testing your ability to solve problems, work under pressure and your personal organisation. It also tests your written communication skills. As you will see later, it is also testing your multidisciplinary team working skills.

There is a large element of crossover between the tasks. Be aware of all the possible elements of assessment for each task. The more you prepare, the more likely you are to perform and score well on the day.

Role play
Introduction & techniques

One of the two tasks that you need to complete is the "simulation" or "role play" exercise. This consists of three scenarios (each with a different actor), lasting 10 minutes each. One scenario is with a patient, one with a relative or carer, and one with a non-medical colleague. Imagine that this is a real outpatient clinic, hospital or GP surgery. Imagine that the "actor" is a real patient, colleague or relative and you will perform much better. The moment people start to think about "acting", things tend to fall apart. This task is not designed to catch you out or make you feel embarrassed; it is there to see how *you, the doctor,* behave when you are with real people. Be yourself, but "play the game".

Playing the game

Those of you who have completed your driving test will know that there are things you do in your test to make sure that the examiner sees you doing them. This is what I mean by "playing the game". In your driving test, you turn your whole head to look in the rear-view mirror, while, in everyday driving, most of us just move our eyes. The role play is exactly the same. You need to make sure that the assessors see you performing certain tasks. To enable them to see you doing this, you need to show them very clearly what you are doing and thinking during the exercise. It is not enough to assume that they have picked up on things.

In an ideal world there would be real patients and colleagues for this assessment. The only way to standardise the task is to put actors in their place but you need to treat the actors as you would "real people".

Make it real

Having worked as an actor patient, I can assure you that, as long as your selection centre is using a reputable company to supply the actors, they are highly skilled, formally trained and very experienced at the roles that they are expected to perform on the day. They want to help you and will do everything they can to make sure that you are on the correct path; but they cannot put words in your mouth and, if you do not pick up on the clues that they throw at you, you will get stuck. If you do not ask them the right questions, it is almost impossible for them to help you gain those all-important ticks in the boxes that will score you points. This is where this book and good quality courses will help you. I cannot tell you what to say word for word, since the exact questions and phrases will be very much dependent on the type of situation that you get; but if you know what the assessors are looking for and you have a framework in mind, then you are much more likely to ask the right sort of questions and succeed.

Listen

The most important piece of advice I can give you for this exercise, and indeed for your clinical practice as a whole, is LISTEN. Patients, relatives and colleagues (and therefore the actors) tell us everything we need to know. Not necessarily in the order that we would want, and not always in an easily identifiable way, but listen, listen, listen. When you go back to work, practise with your own "real" patients and colleagues. Try not saying anything; try using silence; try nodding and acknowledging instead of telling them what is about to happen. Put the patient in the driving seat and see what magical information you receive. Even the person who sits in silence is telling us something. Do we intimidate them? Are they frightened? Are they listening? Are they trying to work out what to say to you? Are they trying to phrase a question but don't know how to ask? Give them the opportunity and see what happens.

Silence

In 1967, the Tremeloes sang a song called "Silence is Golden", and it definitely holds in modern medical practice. I am not suggesting that you sit in silence with your actor for 10 minutes, but often "less is more". The less you say in the opening minutes of the scenario, the more information you will get from the person and that golden information may just point you in the right direction to score well. Try practising it at work. Greet your patient, relative, or colleague and ask them how you can help. Then let them talk for a couple of minutes before you interrupt. See what else you find out. These skills are not just important for the role play assessment; they will also improve your clinical skills and general interaction. Try it.

In the role play, the actor often fills the silence, giving you a clue as to what they want to talk about. This is where the listening can be crucial. Listen to every word they say. If they are repeating the same phrase time and time again, it is often because it is a clue; if you follow it up, it will unlock another part of the consultation that will gain you extra marks.

What will happen?

Once again, read the information sent to you from your selection centre for definitive clarification. All centres now have three scenarios lasting 10 minutes each. It is most likely that you will stay in 1 room for all three scenarios and the actors will come to you and knock on your door. The order will depend on the selection centre but it is certain that you will have one patient, one non medical colleague and one relative/ carer. In some centres, it may be the other way around, and you may be expected to move rooms between each scenario, but this is less likely.

Inside the consultation room with you will be one or two assessors. They will be GP examiners or educational psychologists who are trained to mark you on the strict criteria of the selection centre. Be polite when you enter the room, but ignore them. They are there to mark you, not to help, guide or advise you. Do not worry about them being able to see everything. If they can't see you, they will move. Try to forget that they are present. You may hear them writing throughout your entire assessment; try to ignore it.

Read the brief

Your 10-minute time period may or may not include reading time (it often does). Check carefully to ensure that you do not spend the full time allowance on reading that brief!

Follow the instructions on the day. Read them, read them and read them again. This is just like a referral letter or a handover from another doctor.

It is most likely that your brief will be very vague. For example:

Mrs Ben, aged 35, has come to see you for the results of her test. All bloods and x-rays are normal.

Or

Dorothy, the Health Visitor has asked to chat to you.

Or

Mrs Evans the wife of your patient Mr Evans, has asked to talk to you about her husband. (He has given his consent for you to talk to her).

It is less likely, but it may also be something fairly complicated:

Mrs Ben, aged 35, has come to see for the fourth time complaining of the same symptoms: sleepless nights and cough. She has never coughed up blood and has no sputum production. You have fully examined her every time you have seen her in the past and sent her for numerous investigations including a chest x-ray and routine bloods. All investigations are normal.

Take your time (though, obviously, not too much time either) and read the information. Time after time, I see candidates making assumptions, adding information to that given or ignoring the information given in the brief. If the information is not there, do not assume anything. What would you do in real life? You would check the notes and, if you can't find them, then you would ask the patient.

The role play is no different to your real practice. The information given to you is accurate. If it says that the investigations are normal, that is what it means. Do not assume they have been reported wrongly. Do what you would do in real life. If it says that you have examined her in the past then that is what you have done.

If a patient has given permission for you to talk to their relative/ carer then you can assume that you can talk about everything. Believe what is written down.

Set the room up

If you feel it is necessary, set up the consultation room in a more suitable fashion. There may be points given for "setting up a safe environment" and in any case you will need to ensure that the setup is suitable for the purpose of the consultation and there will definitely be marks for your ability to develop a rapport and engage with the patient. This doesn't mean taking a can of paint and redecorating the walls, but it does mean moving the furniture to a comfortable position.

When you arrive, the chairs may be either side of a desk (Figure 1). If this is not comfortable for you, move them. I am often asked for the ideal set-up and the ideal distance between chairs. There is no right answer to this. You need to be able to see your patient, relative or colleague and they need to be able to see you. You must be close enough to touch the patient (or to hand them some tissues) if required, but not so close that you intimidate them or are touching knees.

Practise at work. Try the chairs in different positions. Try different distances. Try with and without a desk. You will rapidly become aware of what is comfortable for you and for your patients/ colleagues. If you find your patients moving their chairs backwards during a consultation then you are probably too close. If you feel that you need to move your chair forward, then it is likely that you are positioned too far away.

Figure 1 - Poor positioning of chairs.

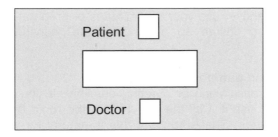

The table is a barrier between the doctor and the patient

Figure 2. Suggested alternative setups.

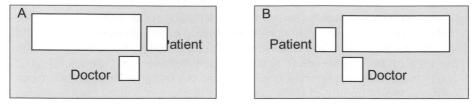

The desk is no longer a barrier. Work out your own preferred distance between the patient and doctor chairs. See what feels comfortable. Try without a desk if that is more comfortable for you.

Assessment criteria / marking scheme

The role play station is designed to test your communication skills (both verbal and non verbal), your empathy and sensitivity, problem solving and, to a lesser degree, your clinical knowledge base (e.g. you may need to explain a condition to a patient). Depending on the scenario, it may also be used to assess your professional integrity, probity, organisational skills and your ability to cope with pressure.

The marking schemes vary from year to year. However, there are some common themes that are likely to feature prominently. These would include:

1 – Creating a safe environment
As mentioned above, use your few minutes of preparation time to set the room up to ensure an adequate "safe" consultation can be performed.

2 – Introduction and putting the actor at ease
Introduce the consultation or meeting sensibly. If you are given the patient's name, use it. Call the patient into the room by going to the door to greet them. Shake hands if this is natural for you and guide them to their seat. It has been known for an actor who is not guided by the candidate to sit in the "doctor's" chair. This can easily be avoided by guiding them. If you are not given a name, introduce yourself and ask for their name.

3 – Active listening and encouragement

Remember: "Silence is golden". Start the consultation with an open-ended question. Give the patient, relative or colleague the opportunity to speak so that you get threads that you can explore during the consultation.

- How can I help today?
- What would you like to talk about?
- How are you?
- You asked to see me...

Choose a phrase that you would normally use to make it as natural as possible. Once you have done this, allow the patient / colleague time to speak, with a little silence if possible. Avoid using closed questions that push the actor towards "yes" or "no" answers, such as:

- Have you come to see me again about your cough?
- I understand that you wish to talk to me about your son, is that right?

Active listening involves making full use of many of your senses:

- Listen to what they are saying – and to what they are not saying.
- Look and see how they are behaving. What is their body language saying?
- Feel the emotions that the actor is emitting and the emotions that they are evoking in you. Are they depressed, angry, nervous or agitated?

By opening in this way you have the added benefit of allowing yourself to settle into the consultation, and for your heart rate to begin to slow down.

Encourage the patient or colleague with prompts and by reflecting on their own words.

- You said you are worried about ...
- Tell me more about ...
- What happened then?

This will hopefully enable you to get a real sense of what the patient wants and thinks. The actor will try to give you as many clues as they can during this opening stage, so LISTEN to every word that they say.

4 – Relevant psychosocial information

This aspect of the consultation is most often neglected by candidates when it is in fact an area where it is very easy to score extra points. All patients and their carers are affected not only by the physical illness, but also by their psychological, financial, social and spiritual states. By incorporating these in your consultation, you will gain a better understanding of the whole patient/ carer.

Colleagues will also have a psychosocial aspect to their presentation in the scenario. Their psychological, spiritual and financial state will influence their behaviour too. Don't forget!

Psychological
- How are you coping?
- How is this affecting you?
- How are you sleeping?

Financial
- Are you still managing to go to work?
- How do you afford to pay for your 8 pints of beer per night?
- Have you applied for any benefits or help?
- Can you afford to take any sick leave?

Social
- Who is at home with you?
- Is there anyone you want me to call?
- What do you do in an evening?
- Do you have anyone to talk to?

Spiritual
- Who do you confide in?
- Do you have a Minister/ Rabbi/ Elder/ Priest you can talk to?
- Do you visit a Temple/ Church/ Mosque for support?

Each individual patient, relative and colleague; and each individual scenario will lend itself to different psychosocial questions, but it is important to cover some aspect of it during your role play. Don't throw easy marks away.

Practise on your patients when you go back to work. Once you learn to incorporate these types of questions into your history-taking, it is amazing how natural they become and how much more relevant information you acquire.

5 – Expectations, including any hidden agenda

Patients often attend wanting something or with an expectation. How many of you have been to visit your own GP and sat in the waiting room, planning not only what you want to say but also how you are going to say it? Our patients do exactly the same thing. A simple way of finding out if there is an expectation is by asking questions such as:

- What were you expecting today?
- How do you want me to help you today?
- Is there anything else I can help you with today?

These simple questions often open doors to hidden information. Try them out in your day-to-day work. See how often there is "something else" that you may otherwise have missed.

Your colleague, in your scenario, may also have a hidden agenda. Don't miss this. A junior nurse who approaches you to talk about her study leave, may really be being bullied by someone at work but be too scared to talk about it openly. Make sure you ask questions to ensure you are not missing anything such as:

- Is there anything else you wanted to talk to me about?
- Is everything else ok at work?
- How are you getting on working here?

6 – Clinical questioning (If appropriate to your scenario)

You need to make sure that you have covered all the relevant questions relating to the presenting complaint in your patient scenario relating to "red flags". By this I mean the danger signs associated with specific diseases:

- In the case of lower back pain, are the bowel and bladder intact? Is there any weakness? If it is a man, is he still having erections?

23

- For a persistent cough, has there been any haemoptysis or weight loss?

In scenarios with the relative and the colleague, you need to ensure you are a "safe doctor". For example, if your colleague has told you about a clinical mistake:

- Is the patient safe?
- Do you need to fill in an incident form?
- Do you need to write in the accident book?

Do not spend the whole scenario on this section. It is often the area that we are most comfortable in, but only a small number of marks, if any, will be given. Cover the essential points and move on.

7 – Explanation and differential diagnosis (if relevant)
Having spent time observing and talking to the patient, relative or colleague, you will have an indication of their level of understanding. Having elicited their psychosocial agenda, you may have found out what their occupation is (assuming the brief hadn't given you the information anyway). You need to match your explanation and/or differential diagnosis to their level of understanding. You will clearly use different words when talking to a Consultant physician than you would if the patient had learning difficulties. Pitch your explanation to the level of the patient, relative or colleague. Using medical words is acceptable as long as they know what they mean. Just because someone is a midwife, it does not mean that they know all about a complicated medical condition. Always check!

8 – Working diagnosis or plan of action
With a patient, it is obviously important to have an idea of a diagnosis and explain a clear management plan; but again there will only be a small number of points for this comfortable area of the consultation (this is what the MCQs and EMQs are for!). If you know what is wrong with the patient, say it and propose a management plan. If, on the other hand, you have no idea what the diagnosis or problem is, then don't panic. Be honest and do what you would do in real-life situations. You would ask a colleague or your boss. You would do further tests or review them again.

- I am not sure exactly what is causing your symptoms and so I would like to do some more tests / ask a colleague of mine to see you / see you again in a few days to review things.

With a relative, carer or colleague it is also important to have plan of action. What are you going to do next? What action are you going to take and what action is expected of them?

- I will write up this meeting and email you a copy to check before we make an appointment to see the Consultant. Is that ok?
- What would you like us to do before we meet next time?

Remember to make the consultation as real as you can. Imagine this is a real situation and behave the way you would do every day.

9 – Choice

If people have a choice in what is about to happen, they are often more compliant with clinical treatment and non clinical management plans. Offer the actor a choice.

With a patient:
- We can either just wait and see what happens, or I could order a chest X-ray today.
- Most of the time this would settle without antibiotics. How do you feel about not having a prescription today?
- What would you like to happen now?

With a relative or carer:
- What would like to see happen next?
- How do you think I can best help you achieve your aims?

With a colleague:
- Who would you like me to talk to?
- Would you like to take this matter further?
- Would you be willing to go and see your own GP or occupational health?

Once again, try this in your everyday practice. People like to be involved. You will obviously meet patients that defer all decisions to the doctor but you are still allowing them a choice, even if that choice is for the doctor to decide.

10 – Checking understanding

It is important to confirm that the patient, relative, or colleague understands what has happened in the meeting; this is another way of "playing the game". Do not assume that the assessor has given you the point unless you have specifically asked the question.

- Do you know what I mean by "viral infection"?
- What do you understand when I use the word "cancer"?
- Is there anything you don't understand or want to ask me about?
- Is there anything that you didn't understand?

These are all ways of showing the assessor that you are checking that the patient understands, and another way to score easy points.

Some people prefer to check the understanding by asking them to repeat part of the consultation:

- Can I just check what you understood when I talked about diabetes?
- Just so I'm sure: can I ask you to talk me through the medication? How often should you take it? When will you take it?
- Humour me, can you tell me what we decided our plan of action is going to be?
- Before we finish, can we summarise our decisions?

11 – Follow-up and review as required

We are now coming to the end of the scenario and it is important that the actor knows what is going to happen next. Let them know when to come back to see you or when you next plan to meet.

- Once your tests are all completed, call and make an appointment for a week later.
- If things don't improve in 3-4 days, please come back and see me.
- If you get worse over the weekend or if you develop a rash that doesn't go away, please go straight to Accident and Emergency.
- Once you've spoken to X, call me; we can arrange to talk again.
- Can we meet in a week's time to see if things are any better?

By adding this kind of comment to the end of a scenario, you are adding an additional safety barrier for the patient, relative or colleague.

12 – Actor's general impression

When working as an actor patient, I was often asked for my opinion of the candidate. There may be a mark to be gained here if the patient felt you were clear, honest and trustworthy. The most common question I was asked as an actor was: "Would you come back and see this doctor?"

It is very easy to say "yes" and give the candidate the point if they followed the above advice. Even if the candidate did not know the diagnosis, or how to solve a difficult problem, as long as they offered follow-up, advice from others and practised safe medicine, I would always score them well. It was just as easy to withhold the point for the high-flying academic doctor who knew a hundred different causes for my symptoms, or told me in minute detail about the complaints procedure but did not communicate clearly or put me at ease. The ideal would be to know the medicine AND communicate well but, on balance, I know out of the two which type of doctor I would rather be, and which type I would rather see. You need to make those decisions for yourself but, for the purpose of the role play, concentrate on your style over and above your knowledge of weird and wonderful diseases.

13 – Body language and physical interaction

In some role plays, there will be marks for maintaining eye contact and for having an approachable and non-threatening manner. This is often picked up on through your body language.

I do not advocate that everyone should sit in the same way with an open body language; but I do suggest that over the days and weeks before your assessment you start to think about what you do with your body during a consultation. Many of us have a habit that we are unaware of, such as eating/sucking on hair, scratching or jiggling legs and feet. None of these make you a bad doctor, none will stop you getting a job; but they can be irritating for the patient and for the assessor. Why allow something that is easy to control to distract the assessor from your fantastic consultation style?

Start watching other people as they consult, in the canteen, at home or on television. Once you become aware of other people's habits you will see how annoying they can become.

Eye contact plays a crucial role in developing a rapport with people. Maintaining eye contact does not mean staring unblinking into your patient's eyes throughout the whole consultation, but simply ensuring that you maintain a good rapport during the whole meeting. Also, through eye contact, you will gain important information about the patient (or colleague) that you are with and their emotional state.

You would be amazed how many people spend the majority of a consultation or scenario looking at the carpet, the desk or up at the ceiling. We all think in different directions. I am a ceiling thinker, by which I mean that, when I'm under pressure and searching for an answer, my eyes drift upwards, looking for inspiration. This is acceptable for brief periods, but please be conscious of where you look and bring your focus back to the person that you are with. It's easy once you become aware.

Start to think about your own and become aware of others' eye contact. You will soon realise what is comfortable, where you look for inspiration and what you need to do to improve things. Don't be put off if, for the first few days, you feel overly conscious, are unable to maintain eye contact or become fidgety. Persevere, work through the initial awkward phase and trust that with time it will become second nature and part of your natural consultation style.

14 – Remaining calm under pressure

I've added this, not because there will be an explicit mark for it, but because it is a very easy way to lose points. If you are given a difficult consultation or meeting and you feel irritated, if the patient becomes angry or your colleague is not listening to you, you may feel tempted to show your true feelings. If you start to feel irritated or annoyed, those emotions will be detectable to the actor and to the assessor. Recognise them early and take a deep breath. Pause and give yourself time to calm down. A good way of getting out of a sticky situation is to reflect the emotion back to the person that you are with.

- I see you are really angry about this.
- I'm sorry you feel so annoyed about this.
- What can I do to stop you feeling so angry about this?

Such comments will hopefully encourage the actor to talk for a little longer giving you even more time to compose yourself, calm down and think of another approach. Try it, practise and work out which phrases work for you. Use your own words. Make it part of your everyday consultation style.

I am sure that, after reading this, you are beginning to realise how much is involved in scoring well in the role play section. You may not be assessed on every individual point above, but if you make sure that you have covered everything you are certain to do well. When you practise role play with colleagues and during the assessment, make sure that you address all those points as much as possible.

Clinical examination

There are usually no marks for clinical examination. Unless specifically told by your selection centre, there is no need to take any examination equipment along with you. The emphasis on clinical diagnosis and management is small. You have already been assessed at Stage 2 on your clinical knowledge. This task is more about your consultation style rather than testing your ability to diagnose an obscure syndrome. In General Practice, if it looks like a dog and barks like a dog, it is probably a dog. It is unlikely to be a rare pink-spotted zebra that just happens to be wearing a dog-style coat with a hoarse voice and barking cough!

If you feel, for completeness, that you would like to examine the patient in your patient scenario, please mention it – there may be a point to be scored. Use this as an example of "playing the game":

- I would like to examine you, but will do so once we have finished here and I can take you next door to the examination room.
- I think it is important that we listen to your chest again. If it's all right with you, I'll do this once we've finished talking before you go home.
- I would like to do your smear test after we have finished talking, is that OK with you?

Whatever you decide to do, please do not approach the actor patient with arms outstretched ready to pull their clothes off. It is very frightening for the actor and, apart from anything else, they're not being paid enough to perform topless!

Communicating in different ways

I cannot emphasise enough times how important it is to treat this role play as though it were a real situation and remember what you normally do in your own clinics and wards.

For some reason, people forget that there are other ways of communicating in a role play when, in actual fact, they use these skills every day at work. Don't forget the use of a pen and piece of paper; these are usually supplied on the desk. To confirm a patient's understanding, we often write things down and draw pictures. If you feel this would help your role play, do it. If you want to refer your colleague to the internet for clarification of a fact then do it. If you want to give a relative an information leaflet, mention it. The general rule is, if it is something you do every day, do it in the scenarios. Don't change your consultation style for the assessment; instead, bring in all the positive things that you do every day to show how good you are.

If you get stuck in a consultation, checking the patient's understanding (see above) is also a good way to buy some time so that you can work out what you are going to say and do next. Try it.

As mentioned, the use of leaflets is also something that you can bring into your consultation. I'm not suggesting that you bring them along with you, but if you think it would enhance your role play to suggest a patient leaflet do so.

- I think we have a leaflet on this at reception. Once we've finished, I will go and find it for you.
- What I'd like to do is give you a leaflet on this for you to read at home. Why don't you come back once you've read it and we can talk again?

If there are other things that you normally do during your consultations, then do them. Use your own style and use your own words. Don't try to regurgitate word for word what is written in this book or what you are told on a course. Try things out and make them your own. Use this assessment preparation as a way of improving your day-to-day consultation style rather than a one-off change in your style for the purpose of getting a job.

How to end

You need to be aware of your own time. By all means, ask the assessor when you enter the room if they will give you a sign when there are 2 minutes left to go. There is usually a bell to tell you when time is up, to stop and move to the next scenario. You may simply be told "thank you", and asked to leave the room, the actor may just get up and leave. It is obviously better to be able to draw the consultation to a natural close by being aware of the time yourself.

Take along a desk clock or watch to put on the table so that you can see how much time you have left. Place it where you can see it easily without disrupting the consultation. Try not to spend time breaking eye contact just to look at the clock, particularly if it is at a sensitive part of the consultation.

If you finish early, it doesn't matter, as long as you feel that you have covered everything. However, if you have finished after 5 minutes then you have probably missed something. Go back to the psychosocial history and try to tease out any hidden agenda that the actor may have.

If you are happy that you have covered everything, end the consultation as you would normally do. Escort the actor to the door if it is comfortable to do so. Thank them for coming and reiterate your specified follow-up.

- Thank you for coming. As I said earlier, call and make an appointment when you've had those tests done and I'll see you again.
- Is there anything else you would like to talk about today?
- Let me know how things go. If they don't improve, then please come back.

Not enough time

If you do not feel that you have covered everything in the time you have, do not worry. Try to end the consultation within the 10 minutes, even if you have not covered everything. The joy of General Practice is that you can arrange to see your patient again very soon, or follow them up with a phone call. Try to find a way of closing that does not feel rushed.

- It looks a though we are running out of time today. Can I ask you to come back and see me tomorrow?

31

> - There are still many things I want to ask you. Could you make another appointment to see me over the next few days?

If you want to show the examiner what you think you have missed you could always say:

> - I still want to ask you about your family and who you have for support and then arrange how we are going to follow you up. Can I call you later to do that?

Even if you do not have time to end the scenario with in this way, don't worry. You will still score points for all the good things you have done during the scenario and remember, no one is going to be perfect at every scenario. Take a deep breath and move on to the next task.

Hidden agenda

This refers to something that the person in your scenario wants to talk about but doesn't introduce as their initial presenting concern. You often have to dig a little deeper to find out what their true worries are. For example, the person who presents with a cough may have lost their father to lung cancer a few years previously and might be worried that they have cancer. If you don't ask about "any other worries" or about their psychosocial history then you may miss the whole reason for the consultation. Giving antibiotics to this patient will not resolve the underlying anxiety, and may not cure the cough.

Scare stories

We have all heard many scare stories about simulated patient/ role play scenarios. Try to block these from your mind. The actors are trying to help you; the assessors want you to do well. The actor may try to push you to see how you react, but no one is trying to make you fail or make you look silly. If you feel that things are running away with you, take a deep breath and try to get back on track. Be honest.

> - I'm sorry; we seem to be going round in circles. Can I recap what we've said so far?
> - I'm not sure we are communicating very well here, would you mind telling me what you've understood so far?

Although a little staged, these types of phrases will buy you a little time to get back on the right track.

All the other scare stories are avoidable if you communicate well. I was recently told of a case where an actor patient stormed out of the room in the middle of a scenario, angry and crying. The doctor was appalled. Surely this wasn't fair? By running the scenario again, it became very clear that the doctor had antagonised the actor patient to such a degree that they responded in the way a real patient would. By rerunning the scenario using phases similar to those above, the patient was allowed to express his concerns and was given time and space to understand the difficult diagnosis being expressed. By going at the pace and level of understanding of the patient, he was unable to become angry. Any signs of anger were acknowledged and explored further.

The actor will behave as a real patient, relative or colleague. You must treat them as though they are a real person in a real situation.

How to prepare for the day

Practise; practise; practise. You can start right now by introducing all of the above principles into your own clinical consultations at work. Try a different approach each day and see what phrases work for you. Keep practising and don't be put off if it feels slightly contrived for the first few days. Do you remember when you first learnt to take a history as a medical student? That too felt odd, didn't it? How does it feel now that you have had years of practising the same thing every day? Normal? Well, that is exactly how you will feel with this. Persevere and I promise that it will all fall into place.

Practising the technique at work is only one step. Use the role play examples in this book, get together with some colleagues that you trust and play them out. You are unlikely to improve if you just read through the examples though. No one can pass a driving test just by reading a book; you need to get in the driving seat and do it for real.

Try playing the different roles (doctor, patient, relative, colleague) in the role play examples so that you see each scenario from different points of view. Look at how others consult. It is amazing how much you learn about yourself by watching others.

Watch colleagues consulting at work. Who do you respect and why? What is it they do that makes you think so highly of them? Talk to your patients and ask them who they think the best doctor is. You will often find it is their own GP because they know and understand them. Often patients will prefer the junior ward doctors rather than the experienced senior consultants because the juniors spend more time talking and explaining. Find a patient that you get on with and ask them what they think is important when they see a doctor. Use whatever you think is appropriate from all these sources to enhance your own practice.

Finally, the gold standard of practice is to find a reputable and well-respected course that will allow you to practise with trained observers/ tutors. Make sure it has a focus on role play and has a small number of candidates. Listen to the feedback and learn from the other candidates on the course. See what works well and what doesn't. Use everything you can to improve yourself.

Figure 3. Main assessment criteria for role play

1. Creating a safe environment
2. Introduction and putting the actor at ease
3. Active listening and encouragement
4. Relevant psychosocial information
5. Expectations including any hidden agenda
6. Clinical questioning (if appropriate to your scenario)
7. Explanation and differential diagnosis
8. Working diagnosis or plan of action
9. Choice
10. Checking understanding
11. Follow-up and review as required
12. Actors general impression
13. Body language and physical interaction
14. Remaining calm under pressure

If you are daunted by the amount of information you need to get into a 10 minute scenario, please don't be. General Practice is based on 10-minute consultations and the scenarios that are presented to you at the selection centres are designed to be completed in 10 minutes.

Some of the role plays in this book are more difficult than those that you will get on the day. This is deliberate. If you practice with difficult scenarios, the hope is that at your assessment, you will not be thrown by anything that is presented to you. By then, you should be able to cope with anything!

To make things easier, rather than remember the 14 points above, we will use a simplified version during the practice scenarios and it is this simplified version that I would suggest you use on the day at your assessment centre.

Figure 4. Simplified assessment criteria for role play

1. **Create a safe environment and read the doctor's brief given to you**
   a. Read, read and read again!
   b. Move the furniture if you need to and put your watch where you can see it.

2. **Introduction and active listening**
   a. Start the conversation sensibly
   b. What is the actor's expectation?
   c. Are you listening, looking and feeling the emotions?

3. **Verbal communication**
   a. Explanations of diagnoses and plans of action should be clear and pitched at the correct level
   b. Clinical questioning (if appropriate) should show safe practice
   c. Have you given the actor choice?

4. **Non verbal communication**
   a. Your body language (did you remain calm?)
   b. Did you pick up on the actor's body language?
   c. Was there a hidden agenda?

5. **Psychosocial influences**
   Psychological, social, financial, spiritual

6. **Checking understanding and close**
   a. Did you specifically ask if the actor understood?
   b. Is there a follow up or next meeting planned?
   c. Did you finish in 10 minutes?

G Role play practice Instructions

How to run a role play

Ideally, there should be three of you, though you can also achieve excellent results with two.

The doctor
One person should take on the role of the candidate (i.e. the doctor). This person should only read the brief for the doctor and nothing else. This way you will make the exercise as real as it can be and comparable to the assessment itself. In each category (patient, relative/carer, colleague) there are 5 detailed role plays. Each category then has 10 other less detailed role plays. For each role play, practice writing the *Simplified assessment criteria for role play* shown on page 35 to remind you of all the points you need to try to cover during the 10 minutes. Paper will be provided to you on the day of the assessment. Use it to remind you of all the points you need to try to cover.

The "actor"
The second person should take on the role of the "actor". This person should only read the brief for the patient, relative/carer or colleague. On the day of your assessment, the actor that enters the room is of the age and gender that you see in front of you. Many of the practice role plays in the book can be played as either a male or female. There are a few that are sex specific so you will need to improvise! Be yourself and try to be as real as you can for your colleague.

I personally think that you can learn as much by being a patient as you can by playing the role of the doctor. Even if the colleagues with whom you are practising are not attending the Stage 3 assessment centre, try playing the patient at least once. It will help you understand not only how difficult it can be to get the information over if the doctor is not asking you the right questions, but also how easy the consultation can become if the correct questions are asked and the right attitude is demonstrated.

Playing the role of the patient will also show you how real emotions can feel whilst in the role; this is how your actor patient feels. They will follow the emotions that are invoked in them during the consultation. If you make them feel angry, that anger will continue until you help dissipate it. If you create an environment in which they feel sad and can cry, this is what will happen.

The observer (preferred but optional)
The third person should be the observer. This person sits and watches the doctor, making notes of what happens during the role play in order to give clear, objective and structured feedback to the candidate playing the role of the doctor. The observer is also the timekeeper. When you first start to practise, you may want to give a sign to state that there are only 2 minutes remaining. As you get nearer to the assessment day, leave it up to the candidate to manage their own time, but stop them once their allocated time is up as would happen on the day. You do not need to comment on the actor's performance. The feedback you give is purely for the candidate/doctor.

Timing

To undertake effective preparation, you will need to spend approximately 20 minutes on each role play, the time being split as suggested below:

Figure 5. Suggested time for each role play

2 minutes	The candidate and actor read the briefs
8 minutes	Play out the scenario
10 minutes	Feedback / Debrief

Notes:
- Some actor's briefs are fairly lengthy. The actor patient, relative or colleague may wish to spend a little more time than the candidate to read the brief in order to fully understand their role.

- Although the role plays will be 10 minutes' long, this will often include the time that it takes to read the brief. I therefore suggest that you train with a time limit of 8 minutes. If the doctor's brief is very short and takes less than 2 minutes to digest, you will have more time for the consultation, though I would still suggest that you stick to an 8-

minute limit, in the knowledge that, on the day of the assessment, with a professional actor, things might take a little longer. Make sure that you spend some proper time reading the brief; you don't want to miss important aspects of the role play just for the sake of an extra 20 seconds of consultation time.

- The 10-minute feedback session is only an indication and you can take as long as you wish. Those who are dedicated may also want to rerun all or part of the role play in a different way once they have read our suggestions to approach the scenario, which would obviously lengthen the session.

Escape

If possible you should try to stay in your role, even if the situation becomes tricky. However, when you first start running the scenarios, you may want to agree on a sign to allow either the doctor or the actor to come out of the role play if you have to. This could be something as simple as raising your hand. On the day, you will not be able to take "time out", so start to work out ways of coping with the difficulties that you encounter. As you get closer to the day of the assessment, do not allow yourself to come out of role. Wait until the debriefing session at the end to discuss the difficulties.

Feedback / debrief

After the role play is finished, it is important to complete the exercise by debriefing. I find that it is better to take it in turns, with each of the three participants having time to talk. Try answering the following questions as a way to start your feedback.

1 – The doctor
- Was it easy? Hard?
- What do you think went really well? Why did it go well?
- What do you think was difficult? Why?
- How did you feel during the role play?
- If this patient came in to see you in your real clinic tomorrow, how would you handle it?

2 – The actor

- Would you come back and see this doctor?
- How did the doctor make you feel?
- Did you have time to explain your concerns?
- Did the doctor get all the information that was on your sheet?
- Why did they get the amount of information that they did?
- What was good?
- What do you wish they had asked you?
- Did you understand everything?
- Did the doctor listen to what you were saying?
- Was there anything that you noticed that might have put you off or irritated you?
- Did the doctor have adequate eye contact with you?

3 – The observer

- How clear was the consultation?
- Did the doctor cover all the points in the *Simplified assessment criteria for role play* (p.35)?
- Did the doctor get all the information that was on the actor's sheet?
- Why did they get the amount of information that they did?
- What was good?
- What do you wish they had asked the actor?
- Did the actor appear to understand everything?
- Did the doctor listen to what the actor was saying?
- Was there anything that you noticed that might have put off or irritated you if you had played the patient?
- Did the doctor maintain adequate eye contact with the actor?

These questions are just a guide as a way to start your feedback. As you practise, you will form your own style of feedback. When others feedback on your performance, treat each comment as a learning point. You may not agree with everything that your colleagues say, but it does not mean that there isn't an element of truth in their comment. On the day of the assessment, all that will matter is what the examiners and the actor will think, and not what you think.

Do not take the feedback that you receive as a negative criticism; instead, view it as an opportunity to reflect on your performance and to improve. If, however, you do not feel comfortable receiving feedback from those who are working with you then try working with other people, or try going to a course.

Above all, remember: if everyone is saying the same thing about your performance, then they are probably right.

What you will find in this book

In the next few sections you will find all the material you need for 45 practice role plays.

- Patient role plays (scenarios 1.1 to 1.15)
- Relative and carer role plays (scenarios 2.1 to 2.15)
- Colleague role plays (scenarios 3.1 to 3.15)

Each of the practice role plays has three parts:

1. **The brief for the doctor**
   (Section H, page 41)
   This text represents what you, as a doctor, know about the patient, relative, or colleague and the circumstances of the consultation. It is similar to the information that you will be given as a candidate on the day of the assessment at the selection centre, and may contain red herrings i.e. information which is not relevant.

2. **The brief for the actor patient, relative/carer or colleague**
   (Section I, page 62)
   This is similar to the information that your actor will get on the day. It will let the patient know a little about the history, their hidden agenda (if there is one), and the points that you as the doctor need to try to find out during the consultation (e.g. psychosocial). In order not to spoil your learning experience, you should ensure that the person playing the doctor has not read this text before the start of the role play.

3. **A discussion on points to raise in the consultation**
   (Section J, page 114)
   For each role play, explanations are given. This section will follow the style of the *Simplified assessment criteria for role play* (p. 35). The first 5 scenarios of each style are accompanied by very detailed explanations showing what is expected of you during the scenario. The explanations for the other 10 scenarios are less detailed but again based on the *Simplified assessment criteria for role play* (p. 35).

Role play practice Doctor's briefs

For patients', relatives'/carers', & colleagues' briefs, see Section I
For discussion points on each role play, see Section J

Role plays with patients

Role Play 1.1 Doctor's Brief

You are based in General Practice.

Mr/Mrs Edwards is coming to see you today for the third time this month, complaining of excessive tiredness. He/she is unable to complete his/her normal day-to-day activity without stopping for a nap at least once per day.

At his/her initial appointment, you examined the patient fully and took a detailed physical history to rule out a serious cause. You requested all routine blood tests, including a full blood count and thyroid function tests.

At the second appointment, you explained to the patient that the results for all the investigations performed were completely normal, and that you could find no physical cause for the tiredness. You rechecked the history and examined him/her again. You suggested a "wait-and-watch" approach, with reassurance.

He/she has returned today with exactly the same symptoms. There are no changes to the physical history, clinical examination or blood tests. You do not need to repeat these.

Role Play 1.2 — Doctor's Brief

You are based in General Practice.

Mr/Miss Dewen, who is newly registered at the practice, comes to see you with lower back pain. He/she attended for the first ever time 2 weeks ago, complaining of acute lumbar back pain following picking up some heavy shopping. At the time, there were no sinister red flag signs(*); his/her physical (including a full neurological) examination was normal. He/she was advised to continue his/her regular activities and was prescribed diclofenac (a non-steroidal anti-inflammatory drug – NSAID) three times a day in addition to over-the-counter paracetamol. He/she was signed off work as cabin crew for an international airline for 2 weeks.

He/she returns today with the same symptoms. The history and physical examination have not changed.

(*) A "red flag" sign is one that would alert you to serious underlying pathology causing spinal cord compression or cauda equina syndrome which, if not decompressed surgically (or, in the case of malignancy, with radiotherapy), could lead to permanent neurological sequelae. In the case of back pain, this would include rapid leg weakness, saddle anaesthesia and bowel / bladder symptoms.

Role Play 1.3 — Doctor's Brief

You are based in General Practice.

Miss Little has booked an emergency appointment. The nurse triage notes say that she has a urinary tract infection (UTI) and will need antibiotics. There is no significant past medical history available to you.

Role Play 1.4 — Doctor's Brief

You are a doctor in Accident and Emergency (A&E) and have just completed an arrest call on a 35-year-old patient called Hilary, who survived. Hilary's partner, who called the ambulance, had found the patient at home. When the paramedics arrived, the patient had no pulse or spontaneous breathing. They commenced resuscitation and were successful. When Hilary arrived in A&E, you took over his/her care and have stabilised him/her from a medical point of view.

Other information
The paramedics found 2 empty bottles of wine and 2 empty medication bottles at his/her side. There was also an apparent suicide note. You have not seen this.

Your senior colleague has asked you to talk to Hilary to find out more and to determine whether Hilary needs a referral for psychiatric assessment.

(Please note: the name Hilary can be either female or male.)

Role Play 1.5 — Doctor's Brief

You are based in General Practice.

Mr/Mrs Tims has made a routine appointment to see you.

The information you have available is as follows:

Past medical history:

- Hypertension
- Type 2 diabetes
- Sleep apnoea

Body Mass Index (BMI) is 40 (morbid obesity).

Role Play 1.6 — Doctor's Brief

Mr/Mrs Fava is a new patient who is seeing you for the first time. There are no old notes available to you, but the nurse who saw the patient for the new patient check has written down that the patient is due to have his/her gall bladder removed laparoscopically in 2 weeks' time.

Role Play 1.7 — Doctor's Brief

Mr/Mrs Brown is a well-known patient of yours, who is of working class and very practical. You know that he/she has advanced bowel cancer and has discussed this with them on many occasions. So far, he/she has coped very well with his/her illness and coped with all of the treatment (surgery, chemotherapy, radiotherapy) but unfortunately the disease has progressed and has now metastasised to the liver. The patient is fully aware of his/her diagnosis.

The last hospital letter available to you states that the oncology consultant wants to put Mr/Mrs Brown into a trial for a new chemotherapy treatment. The small amount of information that you have suggests that the chemotherapy is very toxic and only improves survival by a small amount.

Role Play 1.8 — Doctor's Brief

You are based in General Practice. Mr/Mrs Joyce is a well-known patient of the practice and attends at least once per week. You have never seen him/her before but, from discussions in meetings, you are aware of the patient, who never seems to have anything wrong with him/her despite multiple attendances.

Over the last year he/she has also been referred to the general medical team, who fully investigated him/her; and, since there was nothing seriously wrong with him/her, discharged him/her back into your care.

Role Play 1.9 — Doctor's Brief

Jody is a 15-year-old girl. She has booked an appointment with you. There is no specific past medical history and, in the past, she has attended with her mum, whom you know very well. Jody's mum is a school head teacher and is very strict with her children. For the appointment today, Jody will attend on her own.

Role Play 1.10 — Doctor's Brief

You are based in General Practice

Mr/Mrs Thanopolos is a new patient attending for the first time. There is no medical history and he/she has failed to attend his/her routine new patient check with the nurse. (All patients are expected to see the nurse for their basic measurements, screening examinations and history to be taken prior to seeing a GP in your practice).

Role Play 1.11 — Doctor's Brief

You are based in General Practice

Mr/Mrs Angelman is a long-term patient of yours with chronic pain. You have looked after him/her for many years and have managed to stabilise his/her pain on traditional medication (paracetamol, ibuprofen and codeine). He/she has not been to see you for several months but you had a call from him/her yesterday saying he/she can no longer cope and he/she urgently needed to see you.

He/she is still taking their medication and nothing has changed in the clinical examination. You do not need to examine him/her again.

Role Play 1.12 | Doctor's Brief

You are based in General Practice

Mr/Miss Marley is a patient with chronic psoriasis. He/she has managed his/her condition well over the years and has been under the care of the dermatologist at the local hospital for the last 6 years. Other than prescribing the medication requested by the hospital (topical steroids, vitamin D analogues and moisturisers) you have not had any contact with the patient.

The latest letter from the hospital states that Miss/Mr Marley has now not attended 3 out patient appointments and has been discharged back into your care.

Role Play 1.13 | Doctor's Brief

You are based in General Practice

Mr/Mrs Treacle is a known drug addict, who is on methadone. He/she is usually looked after by one of the GP partners, who is a specialist in drug rehabilitation. That particular GP partner is away on holiday and has left specific instructions for all of his methadone patients in their notes.

In Mr/Mrs Treacle's notes, it states:

Mr/Mrs Treacle is highly addicted to heroin and is on a high dose of methadone. Their prescription for methadone is complete for the duration of my absence. Under no circumstances should any doctor in this practice prescribe more methadone whilst I am away. Mr/Mrs Treacle often tries to obtain more and should be redirected to the drug rehabilitation unit at the local hospital.

Role Play 1.14 | Doctor's Brief

You are based in A&E

The casualty card for the patient Miss/Mr Fathy states:

22:30 Nurse triage

Patient has run out of sleeping tablets. Insists on a further prescription. Advised to attend GP tomorrow. Patient refuses and insists on seeing a doctor.

Role Play 1.15 | Doctor's Brief

You are based in General Practice

Mrs Logan is coming to see you following her recent appointment at the breast cancer clinic.

You referred her to the one-stop clinic 2 weeks ago with a lump in her right breast. You have received the report from the consultant stating she has a high-grade breast cancer and needs to attend the breast clinic urgently to discuss her further management, which is likely to include, surgery, chemotherapy and radiotherapy.

Role plays with relatives / carers

Role Play 2.1   Doctor's Brief

You are based in General Practice.

Mr/Mrs Gregory, whose daughter Ellen came to see you 1 month ago, has come for a general appointment. You have never met him/her before.

Information that you already know from the daughter

Ellen came to see you 1 month ago, as she was worried about her periods. She had been amenorrhoeic (without periods) for 6 months. There was no physical evidence of disease other than being underweight (BMI 17.5). She denied over-exercising or starvation/binging.

On deeper questioning, there were multiple stressors in her life including multiple debts and a split from her husband, which necessitated her moving back in with her parents and sister. She also said that her sister was dying from leukaemia. The sister is not a patient at the practice.

After offering support and explaining to her that the periods were most likely related to her being underweight with the associated psychological problems as a probable cause, you arranged some routine tests and had arranged to see her again 1 week later.

She has not attended any of the planned follow-up appointments and has not had her blood tests taken.

Role Play 2.2 | Doctor's Brief

You are working in paediatrics and recently saw a 10-year-old boy called Gianni with his main carer (Mr/Mrs Evans). He was referred for a psychosocial problem, which resulted in him avoiding school. After numerous consultations with Gianni and the main carer, you have discharged Gianni from your clinic with a behavioural programme that appears to be working. Both the paediatric team and the main carer are happy with Gianni's treatment and progress.

You recently received a distressed call from the main carer stating that their estranged husband/wife is going to come up to the hospital demanding to see the Consultant as they believe that Gianni needs some kind of investigation in the form of a CT scan to rule out a brain tumour causing the change in Gianni's behaviour. The main carer is happy for you to share all the information.

Your Consultant does not think that any investigation is required and will be unavailable for the rest of the day.

The estranged spouse has now come to you. You are the only doctor available to talk to him/her.

Role Play 2.3 | Doctor's Brief

You are based in General Practice. Eddie is the head carer at Tree Tops Care Home, which is located around the corner from your practice. You have never met him/her before.

You have been looking after one of her residents (Hildi) for many years. Her general health is good, but, over the past year, she has begun to decline from a mental health point of view. She has been diagnosed with dementia and is under the local memory clinic, where she is seen on a monthly basis.

Eddie has asked to see you. For the purpose of the role play, you have the permission from Hildi to discuss her care with Eddie.

Role Play 2.4   Doctor's Brief

You are based in General Practice.

One of your patients. Bob Pain, has just been diagnosed with prostate cancer. He is under the care of the urologists and the oncologists; and has just commenced his treatment. The cancer is inoperable and he already has bone metastases. He came to see you last week to discuss his disease and the upcoming treatment. During the consultation, he told you that he did not want his family to know about the prostate cancer.

Bob has not let his family go to any of the hospital appointments. When they ask, he tells them that he has a bladder problem that needs sorting out. His wife has booked an appointment to see you today.

Role Play 2.5   Doctor's Brief

You are based in A&E. Mr Simmons has recently been bought in by the paramedics after a diving accident. He hit the bottom of the pool and fractured his neck. He was intubated by the paramedics at the scene and pronounced brain dead in A&E after a long resuscitation effort.

He was a young and fit man, and in his bag was a donor card.

The team is continuing to ventilate Mr Simmons in A&E until a decision has been made about organ donation. You have been asked to go and talk to the relative to ask them if they will consent.

More information
The relative has already been told by your consultant that Mr Simmons is brain dead. The family have been in to see him to say goodbye and are deeply upset. The consultant did not ask about organ donation and has asked you to go in to speak to Mr Simmons next of kin who is waiting for you.

Role Play 2.6 | Doctor's Brief

You are based in General Medicine, working on the wards.

Jo has asked to see you. He/she is the relative of Mrs Singh who has been an inpatient for 4 weeks following a major stroke. Mrs Singh has been left with a significant expressive dysphagia and a minor weakness in her legs, which means that she now can only walk with the aid of a Zimmer frame, and will need a wheelchair when outside of the house.

Mrs Singh is due to be discharged tomorrow into the care of Jo, who attended a multidisciplinary discharge meeting earlier in the week. At the meeting, Jo was accompanied by Mr Singh (Mrs Singh's husband) and they both agreed that Mrs Singh could be discharged home tomorrow.

Role Play 2.7 | Doctor's Brief

You are based in General Practice.

You have been called by Tracey, a teacher at the local primary school. She is concerned about the welfare of Thomas, a 7-year-old boy who has been coming to school for the last 2 weeks in soiled clothing. Today he arrived at school with severe bruising to his right leg.

Tracey asked Thomas' mum about the bruising. The mum told Tracey that she was taking Thomas to see you today to have it checked as she didn't know how he got the bruise and she was concerned worried.

Since Tracey understood that Thomas would be attending the GP surgery today, she did not contact social services about her concerns, but wanted you to be involved as she felt that this may be a case of abuse and that social services should be involved.

Thomas' mum, Asia, is your next patient. She has booked an appointment for herself. Thomas is not with her.

Role Play 2.8   Doctor's Brief

You are based in General Practice.

Last week you saw a 37-year-old woman (Val) with severe flu-like symptoms. You treated her conservatively as a viral infection and advised her to come back if things became worse. She came back to see you 2 days later, at which point you had to admit her with pneumonia. You had a message from the intensive care unit at your local hospital saying that Val had rapidly deteriorated with septic shock and died unexpectedly last night.

Her sibling, Steph, has asked to see you today. Complete examination of Steph is normal.

Role Play 2.9   Doctor's Brief

You are based in General Practice.

Your next patient is Mr/Mrs Kahn. He/she has not visited the doctor for 12 years. You see the rest of the family regularly.

- The grandmother (82) has recently been discharged from the orthopaedic team following a fractured neck of femur.

- The grandfather (86) died last year following a heart attack.

- The daughter (14) saw you recently following an episode of Chlamydia.

- The son (17) saw you recently as he wants to become a doctor and asked for some career advice.

Role Play 2.10 Doctor's Brief

You are based in General Practice.

Nancy is an 84-year-old patient of yours with type 2 diabetes. She is of sound mind and has full capacity. There is no element of depression. She has already had one leg amputated because of her diabetes and is now in the early stages of renal failure.

You have discussed diabetes with Nancy on many occasions and, every time, she promised to start eating healthily and to take her medication regularly.

You saw her last week at home. She was eating her lunch at the time, which consisted of a jam sandwich and a bar of chocolate for dessert. At that time, you talked to Nancy about her diet and she replied she was fed up with being on a diet and was happy to accept the consequences of her unhealthy eating habits.

You reassessed her capacity and decided that she understood the consequences. At the end of the consultation, you decided that, although you would continue to offer support and regular review, there was little more you could do.

You offered to refer her to a dietician and she refused. You have planned to see her again next week. Her blood marker for diabetes (HBA1C) shows that she has very poor control.

She has a carer, Anja, who visits her twice every day. The carer has asked to talk to you. Nancy has given her consent for you to talk about her with her carer.

Role Play 2.11 — Doctor's Brief

You are based in General Practice.

Your next patient is an emergency patient: Mr/Mrs Amtable. There is no history.

Role Play 2.12 — Doctor's Brief

You are based in General Practice.

Mrs Pullie is the daughter of one of your patients, Edna.

Edna (your patient) was admitted to hospital for a routine angioplasty of her femoral artery 1 month ago. There was a complication and she suffered a major bleed into her retroperitoneal space. After major surgery the same night, she ended up on intensive care and died 1 week later.

Mrs Pullie has made a formal complaint against the hospital for neglect. She has asked to see you to discuss her mother's case.

For the purpose of this role play you have the consent of her mother to discuss her care, even after death.

Role Play 2.13 — Doctor's Brief

You are based in General Practice.

Mr Jay is the husband of one of your patients. He has asked to see you about his wife.

Role Play 2.14 — Doctor's Brief

Trevor is a 52-year-old patient of yours; he has a brain tumour. The treatment failed and he is now receiving palliative care at home. He is on a syringe driver containing morphine and an anti-emetic. After speaking to the palliative care nurses, they expect Trevor to die in the next 24-48 hours. He is comfortable and is in no obvious pain or distress.

You know Trevor's wife (Ann) very well and have asked the palliative care nurses if you can talk to her to break the news about his impending death.

Role Play 2.15 — Doctor's Brief

You are based in General Practice.

Your next patient is an emergency patient: Mr/Mrs Ratnam. The last entry was for a urinary tract infection.

Role plays with colleagues

Role Play 3.1   Doctor's Brief

You are based in hospital and are the on call F2 for medicine. Your 5th year medical student (Andi) has asked to have a quiet word with you.

You have worked with Andi for 2 weeks and he/she is a really good medical student, very conscientious and good at what he/she does. He/she even came on call with you this evening and have really helped you by taking lots of histories and taking blood.

Role Play 3.2   Doctor's Brief

You are based in A&E. You are an F2.

One of the nurses (Denni), who is training to be a nurse practitioner, has asked to talk to you.

You have worked with him/her over the past few weeks and think that they are a good nurse.

Role Play 3.3   Doctor's Brief

You are an F2 based in General Practice.

One of the 2 nurses (Alex) with whom you work has asked to talk to you.

Alex is a new nurse and has only been with the practice for 4 months. The other nurse (Woo) is very experienced and has worked at the practice for 12 years. You like and respect both nurses.

Role Play 3.4 — Doctor's Brief

You are an F2 in General Practice. The health visitor has asked to speak to you.

The receptionist tells you it is about a child called Deavon. You have checked her records and, other than the routine baby checks and vaccinations, she has never been seen at the practice. The last time she attended for a vaccination was 8 months ago. At the time, there were no issues. She is not due another baby check or vaccination for 1 year.

Role Play 3.5 — Doctor's Brief

You are an F2 in General Practice. You are the only doctor in the practice at the current time. The practice is in a leafy middle class area and there is very little ethnic diversity. Being a young doctor attached to the practice, the receptionists tend to chat to you rather than to the GP partners.

One of the receptionists (Stevie) calls and says he/she needs to come and see you straight away to talk.

Role Play 3.6 — Doctor's Brief

You are based in General Practice as an F2 doctor. The midwife (Lee) has requested to see you.

There are only 2 doctors in the practice this week. You and the senior partner.

Role Play 3.7 — Doctor's Brief

You are an F2 based in hospital. You have been given the responsibility of teaching a group of four 3rd year medical students. You have given them weekly tutorials for the last three weeks at 9am and this is your last tutorial today. Three of the students have turned up every week and have been attentive. The fourth (Xen) has never attended; today he/she has turned up and told you that he/she needed to leave after 30 minutes for an appointment.

You are due to complete a feedback form today, which will go to the deanery and will count towards their final assessment.

You ask to see the Xen in private to discuss his/her attendance. You need to discuss what you are going to write the feedback form (below).

Name:
Date:

Yes or no

Tutorials attended: 1.
2.
3.
4.

Overall impression: Poor   Average   Good   Excellent

Any other comments:

_____
_____
_____
_____
_____
_____

Role Play 3.8 — Doctor's Brief

You are based in A&E and are an F2 doctor.

The A&E pharmacist (Mr/Mrs Sunar) has asked to talk to you.

Your recent patients diagnoses include:

Fractured ankle	The patient required a back slab and fracture clinic appointment.
Tonsillitis	The patient was given penicillin.
Tennis elbow	The patient was given Diclofenac and paracetamol and referred to their GP.

Role Play 3.9 — Doctor's Brief

You are an F2 doctor based on the wards. The ward sister (Sister French) has asked to talk to you.

Role Play 3.10 — Doctor's Brief

You are an F2 in General Practice. You are the only doctor on the premises.

The practice nurse, Destiny, is coming to see you.

Role Play 3.11 | Doctor's Brief

You are an F2 based in hospital. You are on a busy medical rotation and your leave is fixed as you have 2 weeks of annual leave after each week of nights that you do.

Your best friend is getting married locally in a couple of weekend's time and you have been invited. You are desperate to go, but you cannot find anyone to cover your weekend of nights. (Saturday and Sunday only). Because of the way the rota is structured, there is very little flexibility regarding swaps. Everyone who could cover for you is busy and in unable to cover.

You are desperate to attend the wedding. After all, this is your best friend since childhood. The only thing left to do is to approach medical staffing and ask them if they would be willing to get a locum. Your aim is to secure the weekend off.

The medical staffing officer's name is Charlie and he has agreed to come over to see you to talk.

Role Play 3.12 | Doctor's Brief

You are an F2 based in Obstetrics and Gynaecology. A midwife (Hans) on the labour ward has asked to speak to you.

Role Play 3.13 | Doctor's Brief

You are an F2 based in A&E. During your shift, a ward nurse approaches you.

Role Play 3.14 | Doctor's Brief

You are an F2 based in general medicine. Your consultant has asked you to discharge one of his private patients. He is unable to go to see her as he has to leave the hospital for 4 hours and will not be available during that time.

You know the following:

- Mrs Day. 82. Admitted 2 weeks ago "off legs". Diagnosed with a UTI and treated. Now no infection is present.

- The patient has requested to go home. She is self-funding her private care and now she is well, does not want to waste "unnecessary money".

- The ambulance is booked for 2 hours time to take her home. The consultant will see her privately in 2 days to review her.

The occupational therapist, Waleed, asks to see you.

Role Play 3.15 | Doctor's Brief

You are an F2 doctor based in General Practice. One of the receptionists (Phil), whom you like and respect as they are always polite and good at their job, asks to chat to you.

Role play practice
Patients', Relatives', Carers'
& Colleagues' briefs

Role Play 1.1 | Patient's Brief

You are playing the role of Mr/Mrs Edwards). You are going to see your GP for the third time this month. You have a good relationship with them and like them a lot. You initially presented because you were tired, run-down and needed to sleep in the middle of the day. Your GP has fully examined you twice and completed routine blood tests that have come back completely normal. On your second visit, the doctor explained that all the test results were normal and suggested a "wait-and-see" approach.

You are still tired and needing to nap in the middle of the day.

Important history that your doctor does not yet know
You are not working at the moment and have chosen to stay at home to look after your three young children (aged 1, 3 and 4). Your partner works away and is spending more and more nights away from home. You are worried that they are having an affair. You are embarrassed to talk about this and will only do so if specifically asked about your home life and relationships.

If the doctor is compassionate and asks about your partner, open up and talk. Initially, refuse any help that is offered as a way of talking to your partner. If the doctor persists or offers alternatives, accept their help.

With your partner being away from home, you are up every night with your 4-year-old child who suffers from cystic fibrosis and is currently very unwell. You need some help at home but your extended family lives far away and you are worried that social services will take your children away from you if they ever find out that you are not coping. If the doctor mentions health visitors or social services, you should become very guarded and frightened about your children being taken away from you.

If the doctor is compassionate and allays your fears of the children being taken away, open up and accept the help.

Role Play 1.2   Patient's Brief

You are playing the role of Mr/Miss Dewen. You are cabin crew for an international airline. You love your job, but you have just been moved from working in the first-class section of the airplane to the economy section. You feel that this is because your new line manager – who has been in the job for 2 months – has taken a dislike to you. You feel that you are being victimised at work and you are frightened that you will lose your job if you make a fuss and confront this manager.

Luckily, 2 weeks ago you pulled your back whilst picking up some heavy shopping and the doctor you saw at the time prescribed some pain killers and gave you a certificate for 2 weeks off work. Those 2 weeks are now over and you are frightened to go back to work.

When the doctor initially asks you about your back trouble, tell them that it has not really improved and that you feel unable to go back to work.

In reality, nothing has really changed since the last appointment and it has not got worse. If anything, things are a little better, but you feel that more time off work will help your recovery. The real reason you want more time off work is that your new line manager will move teams in 4 weeks' time and if you are absent for that time you will not have to work in economy class and face further bullying. As such you feel you have to lie to the GP to get what you want.

If the doctor asks about your work, initially be reticent about the truth but give them a hint that all is not well. If they persist, open up and tell them the truth. In reality, your back pain is much better and you really only want the time off work to avoid your new manager.

If the doctor offers solutions to help, insist that the only thing that will help is to avoid the manager and not go back to work; therefore the only help that they can give you is a certificate stating "back pain" for a further four weeks off work. If they persist and offer alternatives, compromise and accept their help.

Role Play 1.3 Patient's Brief

You are playing the role of Miss Little. This morning, you received a letter from the GP surgery stating that you needed to attend for a smear test. It is the third letter that you have received from them in the last 6 months.

Additional information

You have just returned from a 2-week holiday and have had an amazing time. On the flight coming home, you read an article in a magazine about a celebrity who died in 2009 from cervical cancer at the age of 27. The article said that all women should attend for their smear tests on a regular basis and that there was now a test for a sexually transmitted disease called HPV (Human Papilloma Virus) which, if treated appropriately, can stop you developing cervical cancer.

The article scared you and you are now desperate to have your smear test done as you are worried that you to may die from this preventable disease.

You are not in a stable relationship and had a sexual encounter with a man on your holiday. You did not use condoms and, although you have no signs of a sexually transmitted disease, you are naturally worried.

You booked the appointment as an emergency patient and lied to the nurse about the reason you wanted to attend. You are embarrassed about ignoring the reminder letters, about being overdue for your smear test and about your risk of a sexually transmitted infection. If the doctor asks about your urine symptoms, state that you have none but are worried. Only divulge your concerns about the sexual health and smear problem if they ask more questions!

Your aim in this consultation is to get the doctor to agree to do a smear test today (after the scenario is finished!!!!) and to perform a sexual health screen. Remember that you are embarrassed. Start the consultation off by discussing your "urine infection" and only if the doctor probes further, ask about the smear test.

Role Play 1.4   Patient's Brief

Your name is Hilary (this is both a male and female name). You have been depressed and under the care of your GP, in whom you have great trust, for the last 6 months. You have been drinking more and more and now have 2 bottles of wine every day. You GP wants you to take antidepressants but you do not want to as you are frightened of getting "addicted" to them.

Today, you couldn't cope any more. You've been alone all weekend and just needed to "escape". You didn't want to die, just to fall asleep for a while to forget all the worries that you have. You took 6 paracetamols and drank 2 bottles of wine. There were only 6 paracetamols left (3 in each of 2 bottles). You would have taken more if you had them. It was not planned and you did not leave a suicide note. It was totally spontaneous.

If asked about a suicide note, you did not write one. You were in the middle of writing a quick note to your sister Barbara who was going on holiday to say "goodbye" as you could not face going to see her later in the day, but only managed to write the first sentence: "*Sorry Barbara. I need to say goodbye in a letter…*". The doctor will come and try to find out if this was a suicide attempt. Be shocked and upset: "Of course it wasn't!"

After a few seconds, go very quiet and switch off from what the doctor is telling you. Only when they ask you a direct question should you re-enter the consultation. If the doctor does not try to re-engage you, do not volunteer anything. If they are compassionate and acknowledge that you are "zoned out", come back into the consultation.

If asked, tell the doctor about the depression. Otherwise do not volunteer this information. Be distant. Your GP is the one who can help you. You only want to talk to them. You trust them and they understand you.

If the doctor is kind and caring, then open up to them and tell them the truth. If they do not show compassion, or mention psychiatric assessment, then become cold and switch off again. The ideal situation is for the doctor to listen and to offer ways of supporting you.

Role Play 1.5 Patient's Brief

You are playing the role of Mr/Mrs Tims.

You have finally found the courage to go to your GP to talk about your weight and have made the appointment today to do this.

You are "morbidly" obese and have a BMI of 40. You have high blood pressure, diabetes and a breathing problem causing difficulty sleeping. All those problems are related to your weight.

Time and time again, doctors have told you to lose weight and it has always made you angry. You have always known you are overweight, but have never, until now, been ready to face it and make changes to your life.

You have come to the doctor to get advice about what to do. You don't know where to start. There are so many diets on the market and you don't know which one to choose.

Currently, you eat 8 times per day (breakfast, 11am, lunch, 3pm, pre dinner snacks, dinner, evening snacks and you always have some toast with your milky drink before you go to bed). You do not believe that you eat a lot and think you are eating the correct foods. After all, you cook everything yourself, home made pizzas, burgers, fried bread, and pasta being your favourites at the moment. The quantities that you eat at each meal are huge (2 plates of pasta) although you think this is a normal amount of food to eat.

The reason you want to diet now is that your father has just died from a heart attack and you are worried you may go the same way.

If the doctor is judgemental about your weight, become angry and shout at them. Be defensive. If they are non judgemental, be a pleasant and attentive patient.

Role Play 1.6   Patient's Brief

You are playing the role of Mr/Mrs Fava.

You are a deaf patient and cannot hear anything. You can lip read a little, but only if the person speaking is clear and speaks slowly.

You are attending a new GP surgery as you have recently moved house and want to discuss your up coming operation. You are due to have your gall bladder removed in 2 weeks' time.

Your main concerns are not about the surgery – after all you trust all doctors implicitly. Your worries are regarding how you will be treated by the nurses on the ward, and how you will communicate with people. You do however want to know a little bit about the operation, if the doctor knows anything.

The aim of this scenario is to get the doctor to use alternative ways of communication such as pen and paper or drawing diagrams.

If the doctor covers their mouth, talks quickly or talk too slowly and therefore makes it difficult for you to lip read, switch off from the consultation and look out of the window. Only re-engage with the doctor if the actively try to engage with you by getting into your eye line or touching your arm to get your attention.

Refuse the services of an interpreter and, if asked, say that you do not understand sign language.

Even if the doctor is communicating brilliantly with you, on 2 occasions, pretend you do not understand what they are saying to see whether they try alternative ways of communicating.

Note: It may be helpful to you to use ear-plugs when acting out this scenario to make your hearing worse. Try not to make it obvious to the "doctor" if you decide to do this.

Role Play 1.7   Patient's Brief

You are playing the role of Mr/Mrs Brown.

You have advanced bowel cancer and know that the disease has now spread to your liver. You have had every treatment offered to you so far and coped with it well with the support of your family. The hospital has offered you a new trial for advanced bowel cancer which involved a toxic chemotherapy. After reading about it and talking to your family, you have decided not to proceed with the treatment. You do not want any more intervention and have decided it is time to start looking at the palliative care options and the local hospice.

You have come to tell your doctor the news and to ask what other help is available to you in the final stages of your illness.

If the doctor tries to convince you to have the chemotherapy, get angry and shout at them. If they continue to push the new treatment then walk out of the consultation.

Open the consultation by saying that you have "had enough and that it is time to die......." You are not depressed and are happy that you can finally stop going to the hospital and that, at last, you will be able to spend some quality time with your family.

Ideally you want to die at home but you are frightened that you will die in pain. Do not tell the doctor about your fear of the pain, unless they ask. Ensure that you look worried whilst talking about your death, but only if the doctor picks up on your anxiety, divulge that you are worried about pain.

Role Play 1.8   Patient's Brief

You are playing the role of Mr/Mrs Joyce.

You are lonely and have very few friends. One of the places where you feel comfortable and safe is the GP surgery. You know how busy they are and so, rather than telling them the truth, you keep making up reasons for attending. Every week you make an appointment to see a doctor. The appointment is a morning out for you, you get to see other people in the waiting room and have started to make friends with the receptionists. Last week, they even offered you a cup of tea and a biscuit!

You have been doing this for so long now that you are afraid to tell the truth, and so, again, today, you are attending and will tell the doctor that you are worried that your blood pressure has gone up.

The doctors are usually really nice to you and you never spend much time with them, so you don't feel bad about what you are doing. The last time you attended, your usual doctor was rude to you and so you have decided to try a new one today.

If the GP challenges you about your attendance, break down in tears and become very upset. Only calm down once they apologise and start to engage with you again. Be reticent about telling them about your loneliness and only if they ask you about home twice divulge this information to them.

If they offer you alternative ways of having a day out, at first decline saying that you are happy with your life and, only if they persist, then accept what they offer you.

If asked, you enjoy gardening, cooking and shopping but nothing else.

Role Play 1.9 Patient's Brief

You are playing the role of Jody, a 15-year-old girl who has made an appointment with your GP to ask for the oral contraceptive pill.

You are a mature 15-year-old and have been in a relationship with a 15-year-old boy for 6 months. You are not being pressured into having sex and the boy has not yet asked you. You just want to be prepared in case the situation arises as you are spending more and more time with him and have had some intimate contact together.

Be forthright and confident in your choice regarding the pill. You are not embarrassed and know what you want. Do not leave the surgery unless you get what you want.

If the GP asks you to inform your parents, refuse and tell them that if they inform your parents you will report the GP to the GMC. You have done your research and know that the GP cannot tell anyone about your visit to see them and that they have to give you the pill.

Role Play 1.10 | Patient's Brief

Your name is Mr/Mrs Thanopoulos, a new patient in this practice. When you joined the practice last week, the receptionist made you an appointment with the nurse for a new patient check. You did not attend as you do not believe that nurses are good enough to know about your illness. You have a rare genetic disease (one that runs in the family) called "Petit Papoulo syndrome". You are an expert on this disease and know that all sufferers get stomach cancer at an early age; as a result, 3 years ago, you opted to have a total gastrectomy (a major operation to remove the stomach).

You know that your GP will not have heard of the disease as it is so rare, but as always when you move to a new area, you like to visit the GP to get to know them and to test them to see how open and honest they are.

If the GP admits they know nothing about the disease and asks you about it, then fill them in. If this happens the scenario will run very smoothly and end early. This is the aim. Do not give them any information about the disease unless they ask.

If the GP pretends to know about the disease then be very aggressive with them and tell them that they are a liar and you will never come back to see them again. Walk out of the consultation and only return if they apologise and ask you to go back.

The GP may tell you that you have to attend a nurse appointment. Refuse this and tell the GP that you will never see a nurse as your illness is so rare they can often make mistakes. Do not agree to see the nurse, no matter what the doctor says.

Your brother died 3 years ago of malignant melanoma and you blame the nurse at his GP practice for missing the melanoma when it was at an early stage. You have decided you will never see a nurse for an illness ever again. Only divulge this information is the GP specifically asks about why you won't see a nurse on TWO occasions and only if they are compassionate and show empathy towards you.

NB "Petit Papoulo syndrome" is a fictional syndrome and has been invented for the purpose of this role play.

Role Play 1.11 Patient's Brief

You are playing the role of Mr/Mrs Angelman. You have asked to see your GP urgently as you are no longer coping. You have had chronic pain (in your shoulders, knees and hips) for many years and up until now have managed to carry on with your life.

Until recently, you lived alone in a one-bedroom ground floor flat and managed very well. Two weeks ago, your elderly cousin came to live with you. She is very unwell and is under the care of the palliative care team, who have predicted that she only has a few weeks left to live. You have promised her that she can stay with you and that she can die at "home" with you.

This is placing a tremendous strain on you as you only have a 1-bedroom flat and so, for the last 2 weeks, you have been sleeping on the sofa. This and the extra housework is putting a huge strain on you.

When you first see the GP, tell them your pain is out of control and you need stronger pain killers. If they offer them to you, take them and leave. That will be the end of the consultation.

What you really want is support from the GP. You are scared to admit that you can't cope looking after your cousin as you have made a promise to have her stay with you until she dies. There is no other family that can help. If the GP asks about your home life then be honest and tell them what is happening. Accept any help that they offer you.

Role Play 1.12 | Patient's Brief

You are Miss/Mr Marley. You have suffered with psoriasis all of you life and, until 2 months ago, attended every hospital appointment and used every treatment that the dermatologist prescribed for you. Unfortunately you have never had good control of the psoriasis and have reached the point where you are desperate to try something new.

Two months ago, you met a new friend who uses a Chinese herbal doctor for all of their ailments rather than a traditional doctor and, after some persuasion, you decided to go and see the Chinese doctor for yourself to see if they could help you.

They told you to stop all of your conventional medication and prescribed herbs instead for you, which you have now been taking for 6 weeks.

You have decided that you no longer want to use conventional medicine and want to see your GP to explain as you have now received 3 letters from the hospital, the last one stating that you had been discharged. You are happy to have been discharged and do not want to be re-referred.

If the GP tries to convince you to use the conventional medication or tells you that Chinese medication is not going to help you, then stop talking and just nod in agreement with everything they say. No matter what the GP says to you, you are not going to change your mind, but you do not want a fight.

The ideal scenario would be if the GP listened to why you wanted to try the Chinese medicine, asked open questions, allowed you time to talk about how upsetting the psoriasis has been all your life and gave you the option of coming back to see them if you decide to use conventional medicine again.

Be calm and reserved throughout the scenario, even if it does not go the way you want it to.

Role Play 1.13 | Patient's Brief

You are Mr/Mrs Treacle. You are a heroin addict and have been for many years. 8 months ago, you started a programme to come clean and have been taking methadone ever since. You always see the same GP partner at the practice who supplies your methadone. Your usual GP is currently on holiday and you have a full prescription to last until his return next week.

Knowing that your usual GP is away, you have decided to try and get more methadone to help you through the week. You have deliberately booked an appointment with a junior doctor, as you know it is often easy to get what you want from them. Tell the doctor that your prescription for methadone was stolen when you were mugged yesterday. Do whatever you can to convince the doctor to give you the script.

Ideas: try as many as you can in the time allowed.

▪ Cry – tell the doctor you are traumatised after the mugging and you can't cope without your medication
▪ Be angry – threaten the doctor. Tell them it's your right to have the methadone you need.
▪ Be cunning – Lie and tell the doctor that your usual GP often gives you extra in times of trauma
▪ Become frantic – show complete desperation. You need your prescription and you need it now.

When the doctor tells you to go to the local hospital clinic, refuse. Tell them you can't, make up whatever lie you can to convince the doctor to give you more methadone. Even a small amount, just enough for today...

Before the scenario ends, agree to go to the hospital tomorrow for your prescription. Tell them there is no way you can go today and so all you need is a small amount of methadone to se you through the night.

Your aim is to get some methadone, and even a small amount would be a victory for you. The doctor should not give you any; see if you can outmanoeuvre them!

Role Play 1.14 | Patient's Brief

You are playing the role of Mr/Miss Fathy. You have attended A&E in desperation. You are exhausted. Your husband/ wife is currently in intensive care following a motorcycle accident and the doctors today have told you that he/she is likely to be brain dead and they have commenced brain stem testing with a high probability of turning off the ventilator tomorrow.

You have been visiting him/her now for 2 weeks and have spent approximately 20 hours per day in the intensive care unit. You are mentally and physically exhausted.

You have just left the intensive care unit at 22:00 and know that tomorrow is going to be a very hard day. You are frightened that you will not be able to sleep and know that you need to rest to be able to cope with tomorrow.

As you were leaving the hospital, you decided to stop by A&E to ask for some sleeping tablets. You only want 1 or 2, just for tonight. You have never taken them before and do not have time to go to your GP tomorrow as you have to be back at the hospital at 08:00 to meet the consultant to discuss your husband/wife's management.

If the doctor refuses to give you the tablets, cry and do not stop crying until either they give you the tablets you want, or until the time for the role play is over.

If they offer the tablets straight away, take them and do not divulge any personal information at all. Only if they specifically ask about your home and social life, tell them about your partner. Otherwise just keep asking for the tablets on a vague pretense.

Role Play 1.15 Patient's Brief

You attended your GP practice 2 weeks ago with a lump in your breast. Your GP immediately referred you to the breast clinic, where you were examined, had a scan, a mammogram and a biopsy all on the same day.

You are due to go back to the clinic tomorrow for the test results and are really worried that you have breast cancer. You have no family to support you and want to talk to your GP before going to the hospital for moral support.

You are not expecting to be given the results by your GP today; you simply want to talk about what happened and about what may happen if it is cancer when you attend the clinic tomorrow.

The GP actually has your results and it is breast cancer (but you don't know that). If they don't tell you the diagnosis, then continue to ask "What will I do if it is cancer?" over and over again.

If they do tell you the diagnosis then be shocked. Go quiet and refuse to accept the diagnosis. Tell the GP they must be wrong.

The aim of the scenario is for you to leave the consultation feeling that you can cope with the diagnosis of breast cancer and that you know you can always go to see your GP for support.

Role Play 2.1 — Relative's Brief

Your name is Mr/Mrs Gregory. You are attending a new GP as you are desperate. It feels as though your whole life is falling apart. You are happily married and have two children. Your youngest daughter (Ellen) recently moved back into the house after a split from her husband and has stopped eating. You believe that she is suffering from anorexia after watching a recent documentary on the television. She has lost weight and last week you found four different types of laxatives in her bag. She attends the gym every day and no longer eats with the family. You have confronted her and she denies that there is any problem.

You spoke to her estranged husband. He is also worried about her weight. He told you that she had recently been to see her GP but that he did not know what it was for. You want information from the GP. You know that your daughter is a patient there and want to check if she has recently visited the practice, what was said and if she is getting any help with her weight/anorexia problem.

If the doctor refuses to engage with you about your daughter and offers no alternative, become angry and, if no resolution is put forward, storm out of the room.

If the doctor tries to re-engage in conversation, listen and respond to any advice or help that they provide. Deep down, you know that the doctor cannot give you any information about Ellen, but you do not know what else to do. You feel that you are the only one who cares.

If the doctor does give you information about Ellen, keep pushing to see how much information you can get out of them.

You want help not only for Ellen, but also for yourself. Do not divulge this information until the GP asks you about your feelings. You are finding it really difficult to cope and you really need someone to help you through this and to guide you. If the doctor does not offer any solutions then become upset and disengage from the consultation. Accept any help that is offered.

An ideal ending would be to have a follow-up appointment offered for yourself and some form of contact offered for your daughter. This could be a joint appointment if that is suggested.

Important side issue

You have another daughter (your eldest daughter Sarah), who was diagnosed with leukaemia. She has now completed her treatment and is in remission.

At some point in the role play, the doctor might mention that he knows that Sarah is actually dying of leukaemia. This is information that he will have obtained from your daughter Ellen and which is incorrect (i.e. Ellen lied about it in order to make the GP believe that she was experiencing a lot of stress). If the GP mentions that Sarah is dying, then first accuse him of lying and then accuse him of withholding information from you (does he know something that you don't know?)

Role Play 2.2   Relative's Brief

You are Mr/Mrs Evans and have a 10-year-old son called Gianni. You split up from your husband/wife 3 years ago and Gianni lives with them. You do not live with Gianni. He only comes to stay with you at weekends; you have noticed that he is withdrawn and you know that he has not been attending school.

Your best friend was diagnosed with a brain tumour 6 months ago and has just died. Do not tell the doctor this unless you are asked about your worries, but your main concern is that Gianni has a brain tumour too. Before your friend was diagnosed, they became withdrawn, agoraphobic and had significant personality changes. Your friend was diagnosed late and was unfit for surgery. You do not want Gianni to die and want everything done that is possible. You are willing to pay privately to have a scan.

There are big issues between you and your estranged partner and deep down you know that this is affecting Gianni's behaviour. If the doctor suggests that this may be the cause of the problem, become verbally aggressive and accuse them of not treating your son properly.

You are adamant that your son needs a CT scan of his head and are not happy that you have not been involved in the hospital management.

From the start, be angry and demand to see the Consultant unless the doctor explains clearly that they can help. Demand also that your son has a CT scan of his head. Only calm down if the doctor is compassionate and recognises your distress. If they communicate well, you will accept that the CT scan is not required and realise that there are risks with radiation if the medical profession does tests that are not indicated.

Accept any offer of help relating to talking about your friend's death and relationship counselling to help Gianni with his behaviour.

Role Play 2.3 | Carer's Brief

You are Eddie, the head carer at Tree Tops Care Home. One of your residents is called Hildi. She has been living at Tree Tops for 14 years and all of the staff and the other residents love her. She has always been a gentle and kind lady and has been part of the community at Tree Tops.

Hildi has deteriorated over the last year and you are now struggling to cope with her at Tree Tops. She has become forgetful and occasionally aggressive. You now feel that she can no longer live at Tree Tops but do not want to be the one to make the decision that she has to leave and move to a nursing home.

Yesterday, you had a team meeting at the care home where you suggested to the rest of the staff that Hildi may have to leave and move to a nursing home. They unanimously said that they did not want her to leave and that they would all do what ever was required to keep her at the care home.

You have spoken to Hildi's daughter, who does not want her to move to a nursing home and she told you that Hildi had requested to stay at Tree Tops for the rest of her life.

You are now in a difficult position. You, as the manager, believe that Hildi needs to move to a nursing home for her own safety and to ensure that your staff are not overworked. Your staff do not think she should move. Her relatives do not want her to move and you now have information that Hildi herself did not want to leave Tree Tops.

You have requested to talk to Hildi's GP to gain support for your decision to move Hildi. Your aim is to get the GP to say Hildi has got to move and you will then not be responsible for the change. Do whatever you can in the meeting to get the GP to say Hildi has to leave and if possible try to get the GP to agree to put it in writing.

Role Play 2.4 | Relative's Brief

Your husband, Bob Pain, has been acting strangely over the last 2 or 3 weeks, which worries you. He has had several appointments at the hospital and with his GP and will not let you go with him. You know there is something serious wrong with him but every time you try to discuss it with him, he tells you not to worry, that it is just a "bladder problem" and that he is on antibiotics for it.

You are very worried. He looks as though he is in pain all the time, he is not sleeping properly and you have seen blood in the toilet.

You have been researching on the internet and are convinced he has bladder cancer.

You have decided to visit Bob's GP to find out exactly what is going on.

You are determined to get answers out of the GP. Be very demanding and insist that the GP tells you what is wrong with your husband. You believe it is your right to know what is wrong with him; after all you have been married for 25 years.

If the GP tells you he has cancer, be very pleased and end the consultation there even if it is within 2 minutes of starting. Tell them that you need to go and talk to your husband.

If the GP tells you that they cannot give you any information and that you need to talk to your husband, get angry. Shout at the GP and tell them you insist on knowing. Tell a few lies and say:

- I know he has cancer, why won't you talk to me about it.
- I have read hospital letters have seen the word cancer on them.

Your aim is to have the GP confirm your husband has cancer, which is your worst fear.

Role Play 2.5 | Relative's Brief

You are the mother/father of Mr Simmons who has just had a diving accident and you were told 45 minutes ago that he was brain dead. The consultant who came to talk to you explained that he was still on a ventilator and as a family you wanted it kept that way until his children had been to see him to say goodbye.

The whole family have now been in to see him and you are expecting the consultant to come back to tell you that they are ready to turn off the ventilator for your son to die.

The doctor who comes in is not the consultant. Be irritated by this. Is the consultant "too busy" to come and talk to us?" "Who are you anyway?"

The doctor will ask you about donating your son's organs. Refuse. You do not agree with organ donation and do not care what the doctor wants. You want your son to die peacefully and not be cut open by "scavengers looking for bits of him to spread around".

When the doctor tells you that he carried a donor card, tell them that you do not believe them, that your son was a good man and that he should be buried whole and not "cut to pieces".

Remember you are upset and are still coming to terms with your son's death.

Do not agree to organ donation during the consultation. If the doctor insists several times and makes you feel uncomfortable, don't get angry; just walk out of the room.

Role Play 2.6 | Relative's Brief

Your name is Jo. You are the son/daughter of Mrs Singh an elderly lady who has been in hospital for 4 weeks following a severe stroke. You live with her and your father. Before her stroke, your mum ran the house and did everything. She is a very strong lady. Your father does very little around the house and relies on his wife for everything. Whilst she has been in hospital you have been looking after your father, doing all the cooking, cleaning and shopping and also visiting your mum every day. You have had to take the last 4 weeks off work (unpaid) and are exhausted.

Your family's expectation is to have mum home and your father is adamant that she should come home as soon as possible. You feel that you will not be able to cope with both of them at home and have to go back to work next week as, financially, you are beginning to struggle.

You attended a meeting earlier in the week, where the nurses, doctors and therapists were all present. Your father was also there. You did not feel able to tell the truth (i.e. that you cannot cope) about having your mum home and so you agreed to her discharge.

You have now decided to see the doctor to tell the truth. You cannot cope with your mum coming home but you don't want them to tell your dad that you have said this.

Your aim is to have your mum stay in hospital and for her to be discharged home only if she has full time carers to go with her. If this is not possible, you will have to ask for her to go into a care home.

You are polite, often very quiet and do not like looking people in the eye. Try not to get eye contact with the doctor at all. Say as little as possible during the scenario after your opening statement, which should be along the lines of: "Doctor, I'm sorry, mum cannot come home tomorrow"

Use a lot of silence. Nod to agree and shake your head to say no. Try to say as little as possible. Let the doctor do most of the talking. Do not agree to her discharge tomorrow at all.

Role Play 2.7 Relative's Brief

Your name is Asia. You have booked an appointment to see your GP to ask if you can have an insurance form signed. You were due to go on holiday and, unfortunately, you fell and twisted your ankle. You attended casualty and have a letter from them, but your insurance company has requested you get your GP to sign the form.

The only thing you want to talk about is the form. Your aim is to get the doctor to agree to sign the form and then to leave. Try not to get into a conversation about anything else.

Start the scenario by saying (as you enter the room and before you sit down):

It's just a quick one today. Can I get you to sign this form to say I injured my ankle? I've got the letter from casualty as proof."

If the doctor tried to get you to sit down, decline initially saying:

No, I don't need to sit, thanks, I just need a signature from you and then I'll go…

You are the parent of a 7-year-old boy called Thomas. He is a very difficult child and you are struggling to cope with him as a single parent (Dad left when he was 2 years old). Since you've had your injured ankle (for the last 2 weeks) you have found it difficult to do everything around the house and you know that you have neglected Thomas a little. You even sent him to school in dirty clothes this week as you are struggling to walk around the house and do the washing and ironing.

Yesterday, he fell off the shed roof whilst playing in the garden and received a large bruise to his leg. There was no other injury. You are embarrassed that you are struggling to cope with him and also that you did not see him fall as you have left him to play in the garden alone.

When you picked him up from school today, the teacher started to ask you lots of questions about Thomas, and you got scared. You lied, saying you did not know how he got the bruise and will take him to the GP today. You are worried that the teacher is poking her nose into your business and you have seen on the TV that once social services get involved, your child will often be taken away from you.

If the GP asks about Thomas, say he's fine. Do not admit to struggling to cope with him or his bruising, unless the doctor asks directly. If he mentions social services, be scared. Try to stop the GP telling social services at all costs.

Role Play 2.8 Relative's Brief

You are Steph, the brother/sister of a 37-year-old woman called Val and have been staying with her for the last 3 weeks while your home was being renovated. Val became ill last week with a cold and although she was seen by her GP got worse and ended up being admitted to hospital. She died last night.

You are obviously in shock and very upset. You feel guilty as you wish you had taken her to hospital last week and believe that if you had she would not have died.

You do not blame the hospital or the GP and believe that the treatment she was given by everyone was excellent. You blame yourself.

You woke up this morning with and sneezed 3 times. You are worried that you have caught Val's cold and will end up getting pneumonia just like her. You rang the hospital and spoke to the intensive care doctor who told you to go to see your GP to get some antibiotics- just in case.

You have no other symptoms.

Ask the GP for antibiotics and if you get them, be happy and leave. There is no need to stay for the whole 10 minutes.

If the GP asks you questions then be honest. You are upset and shocked. You are worried you too may die. This is the ideal outcome of the scenario. You need to talk to someone and need reassurance that you are not going to die.

If the GP refuses to give you antibiotics then tell them you blame them for Val's death (even though you don't) and that you are going to sue them unless they give you the antibiotics.

Role Play 2.9 | Relative's Brief

You are Mr/Mrs Khan. You are furious. Your 14-year-old daughter Manji told you last night that she was taking antibiotics that the GP had given her. She refused to tell you why she had seen the GP and so you searched her room. You found a leaflet on Chlamydia. You confronted Manji who eventually admitted that she had seen the GP following some vaginal discharge and that she had been treated for Chlamydia.

You are planning to tell the GP off and then to put in a formal complaint. You believe you should have been consulted and that, as a 14-year old, Manji should not have seen the GP alone. You are her parent and have the right to know everything that is going on with her.

Shout at the GP. Point your finger at them accusingly. Be angry throughout the scenario if the GP does not alleviate your anger.

If the GP refuses to tell you anything and does not do anything to calm you down, after 5 minutes, end the consultation and leave.

If the GP refuses to tell you anything, but engages with you talking "hypothetically" about the care of teenagers, then engage with them. Calm down and start to listen. If they do well, by the end of the scenario you should not be angry any more and should not want to put in a formal complaint.

The aim for you is to understand that the GP treated your daughter appropriately and that they cannot break your daughter's confidentiality.

Role Play 2.10 | Carer's Brief

Your name is Anja and you work as a carer. One of your patient's is a lady called Nancy. She is an elderly lady who has lost a leg through diabetes. You like her a lot and often spend longer than you should with her as she is so nice.

You went to see her yesterday as normal and she told you that she is no longer going to take her medication for diabetes and has decided that she does not want to diet anymore. She said it is time for her to die.

You are very concerned. You do not want Nancy to die and insisted that she took her medication. She told you that her doctor knows and that she will not change her mind.

You have decided to go and see Nancy's doctor to find out what you can do to force Nancy to take her medication.

Be caring and kind. You are a gentle woman and listen attentively to everything the doctor is saying. Act in disbelief if the doctor tells you it is up to Nancy. Insist that she does not know what is good for her and ask "how can an old lady make decisions like that?"

You are a very religious person and attend church weekly. You do not believe people should be left to die as every life is worth living and saving.

Role Play 2.11 | Relative's Brief

You are Mr/Mrs Amstable. Your son (Asim) has just returned from university for his holiday. You are very concerned about him. He has lost weight, is not eating, is staying up most of the night and sleeping most of the day. He is smoking excessive amounts of cannabis and admitted that he has used cocaine whilst at university.

His behaviour is erratic and he is intermittently aggressive. He has stopped caring for himself and does not shower. He has not changed his clothes for a week. He is withdrawn most of the time.

At first, you thought it was all due to the drugs use, but yesterday you saw him talking to the television. Later on, you asked him about it. He told you that the house was bugged and that you all needed to leave. You asked him to come to see the doctor with you, but he refused. He said he could not leave the house since as soon as he did, the CIA would enter and implant more surveillance devices.

You think he needs psychiatric care but don't know what to do as he has refused to leave the house.

You want help from your GP. You do not know where else to go.

Role Play 2.12 Relative's Brief

You are playing the role of Mrs Pullie. Your mother Edna recently died in hospital. She went in for a routine procedure and died as the result of a complication. She had to have major surgery and was then on ITU for 1 week before she died. You are devastated at the loss and very angry at the hospital.

Although you understand that complications occur in routine procedures, you know that there was an element of neglect towards your mother.

You worked as a ward nurse until 2 year ago and know a lot about post-operative care. You were with your mother when she came back from her angioplasty and know that the nurses did not check her blood pressure for 2 hours after she returned. During that time, you were worried about your mother and asked 6 times for a nurse to come and review her observations. They were too busy and did not attend. 2 hours after she returned from her angioplasty, your mother suddenly stopped talking to you and looked drowsy. You pressed the emergency button. 2 nurses ran to her bedside, but by then it was too late. Your mother was unresponsive, had an unrecordable blood pressure and the arrest team were called.

She was taken into theatre where a major bleed was found. She never woke up after her operation and died in ITU a week later.

You are determined to get justice for your mother, but are struggling to get any response from the hospital. They said they are "looking into your complaint". You feel that you are being ignored. You just want to go and talk to someone but the consultant and his team have refused to see you because there is an investigation pending.

You want support from your GP. You want to talk to them as you are increasingly frustrated that the hospital team will not talk to you. You just want the GP to listen.

Role Play 2.13 | Relative's Brief

You have been married to Mrs Jay for 12 years. You are worried about her at the moment as she is in a lot of pain. You suspect that she has rheumatoid arthritis. Her mother suffered from the same disease and you recognise the symptoms.

She has pain in the morning and is very stiff. 3 times last week, she could not get down the stairs as she was in so much pain. She had to shuffle down on her bottom and it took her 45 minutes. She is sleeping for 4 hours in the day and has lost weight.

You know that, if it is rheumatoid arthritis, she needs to see someone urgently, as the quicker she gets her treatment the better.

You know that she is frightened as her mother was severely crippled by the rheumatoid and died from a complication. You know your wife is scared that she will die the same way.

You don't know what to do. You have told your wife she needs to see the doctor and she has refused.

You want to try and get the doctor to come home to see your wife and to do an unexpected home visit. Tell the doctor that you will lie to your wife to keep her at home and that if she refuses to see you in the home, then you will "hold her down" until she listens to you.

You know she needs help and you feel helpless. You are her husband and should be able to look after her.

Role Play 2.14 Relative's Brief

Your name is Ann and you are married to Trevor. He is currently at home and is being attended to by palliative care nurses. He has suffered a brain tumour and unfortunately the treatment did not work. Trevor chose to stay at home to die and has been at home in his bed for 6 days now. He sleeps most of the time due to the drugs that he takes through a syringe driver, but for a couple of hours per day he wakes up, you hold hands and you talk to him or read to him from his favourite book.

You are not ready for him to die. You know it is going to happen, but the doctors at the hospice told you it will probably be a couple of weeks. He has been at home for 6 days and so you expect him to be with you for another week.

The doctor is going to tell you that Trevor is likely to die in the next couple of days. Tell him/her that they are wrong. Explain that the hospice doctors are experts and that they said he had another week left. Bargain with the doctor as much as you can. What can he/she do to keep him alive for longer? Tell them you are not ready for him to die.

You are frightened of being alone with him when he dies. What will you do? Who do you call? Only tell the doctor this if they probe into why you want to keep him alive.

Be subdued and upset. Touch the doctor's arm when you ask them to keep him alive. If the doctor pulls away from you, then be offended. If they let you touch their arm, then let go after a couple of minutes.

Your aim is to get support and to know what to do when Trevor dies.

Role Play 2.15 | Relative's Brief

You are Mr/Mrs Rahman, the main carer for your son Noon, who has severe autism. Your husband/wife works away form home and is only there for support 1 weekend per month. You are exhausted and need help.

Noon is 4, does not speak, sleeps for only 3 hours at night and has "tantrums" during the day where he screams for 2 hours at a time. He is still in nappies. He eats, but you have to feed him.

He is now so big that you are struggling to lift him.

He goes to a special needs school from 9am until 3pm, but the rest of the time you are on your own.

You desperately need help but don't know how to ask.

Tell the GP that you are thinking of calling social services to ask them to take Noon into care as you can no longer cope. You do not want him to be taken into care, but you are at the end of your tether and do not know what else to do.

Accept any offer of help that the GP gives you. Be thankful and appreciative. You are a nice patient.

Role Play 3.1   Colleague's Brief

You are Andi, in the final year of your medical school training and are working very hard towards your final exams. Part of your current attachment is to shadow an F2 on the wards in preparation to starting work in a few months' time.

You are on call. You have just attended and watched an arrest call. You ran to the scene of an 86-year-old man who the nurses told you was having chest pain and then suddenly collapsed. When you arrived at the bedside, the arrest team was already working on the man and were just defibrillating him. Unfortunately he did not survive.

You are very upset and frightened. You have never seen anyone die before and have never witnessed an arrest call before. You thought the way the doctors and nurses were doing chest compressions was barbaric and you do not feel that the man had any dignity in his death.

The experience has made you want to reconsider doing medicine. You are not certain you are cut out for the job.

You have asked to see your F2 mentor and want to discuss with him leaving medicine.

Open the conversation by saying that you think you want to drop out of medicine and you do not know who you should contact to enable you to officially leave the course.

Only if the doctor specifically asks you about the reason why, tell them about the arrest call. Initially just keep saying you are "not cut out for medicine". Once you start to talk about the arrest call, cry. You have been really shocked and traumatised by what you saw.

Your aim is to get some support and to have a "shoulder to cry on" rather than to get the information about who to go and see to "drop out".

If the doctor does not show empathy towards you, just tell them you have to go and leave the room after 5 minutes.

Role Play 3.2 | Colleague's Brief

You are Denni, an experienced A&E nurse, and have recently started working towards your nurse practitioner qualification.

You have been given an assignment by your college tutor to complete an audit within the department. You don't understand what an audit is, and have no idea what subject you should do.

You respect an F2 whom you have worked with recently and have asked to see them as you want to get information on what an audit is, how you would perform one and to see if they have any ideas of a topic.

Be very matter of fact. You have no problems at all, are happy in your job, have a great work life balance and are doing well at college. If the doctor keeps asking questions about how you are, tell them off. Tell them to mind their own business and go back to asking about the audit.

Role Play 3.3 Colleague's Brief

You are Alex, a recently qualified practice nurse who has only been working in General Practice for 4 months. This is your first job. You love working with the patients and love the practice. There is one other senior nurse (Woo) whom you work with and who has been at the practice for 12 years. She is very good at what she does clinically, but is messy and lazy.

You have just found out that you are supposed to share all of the non-patient jobs in the practice such as:

- Emptying the clinical waste bins.
- Ordering the vaccinations.
- Cleaning the store cupboard and fridge on a regular basis.
- Updating the practice audit on smoking cessation after every smoking cessation clinic that you do.

When you first arrived, you did not know that you were supposed to share these tasks as Woo gave you your induction and, at the time, told you that all of the above things were your responsibility. It is only by chance today that you found out that Woo should be performing some of these tasks when, at a lunch time meeting, the old nurse whom you replaced (Dez) spoke to you about problems that she had had in the practice. She told you that Woo was lazy and one of the reasons Dez left is that she couldn't cope with Woo refusing to share the workload.

You do not know what to do. You like Woo and other than noticing that she is a bit messy when you use her consultation room, and that she tries to avoid doing any additional work that the practice manager passes on to the nurses. She is ok to work with. She is a very old fashioned nurse and very strict.

You have asked to talk to one of the doctors today to get some advice as to what to do.

Your gut feeling is to do nothing. To carry on doing all the extra work but Dez (the nurse who left) has told you that you should either go to the practice manager or confront Woo.

Role Play 3.4　Colleague's Brief

You are Nikki, a health visitor and are attached to a GP practice.

You have a mum and baby on your books whom you are worried about and want to talk to someone. Mum is a known drug user, who has been clean for 3 years. She has a 3-year-old child (Deavon).

Mum attends regularly to see you in the health visitor clinic to get Deavon weighed and to ask for advice. Deavon is always clean and well cared for, she is growing normally and all her immunisations are up-to-date. You have not witnessed any difficulties between mum and the child; but you have a "feeling" that something is wrong. You are concerned that mum is back on the drugs. You do not have any information about a partner/father.

Although you have no evidence of this, you have now convinced yourself that Deavon is potentially at risk (from neglect) and have tried to refer her to social services. The duty social worker has told you that they cannot investigate on a "whim" and at the moment there is no case for them to take.

You have asked to see one of the GPs at the practice to discuss it.

Additional information (only divulge if the GP asks specific questions)

Two years ago you were the health visitor to a drug user who was "clean". During your time looking after her, she went back on the drugs and overdosed. She died in her flat and her 2-year-old child was found 2 days later next to her body after a neighbour heard him cry. You are frightened the same thing is going to happen again.

At the time, you had no support from other agencies (social services, GP) and so your aim this time is to get as may people involved, just in case of a problem, to ensure that you have support. You also want to ensure that someone else than you sees the mother and child to ensure a better assessment.

At the start of the consultation, ask the GP to help you refer a child to social services. Be very non-committal about the risk that you perceive and only if they ask about WHY you are worried with no evidence, tell them about your other case. If they don't ask WHY, then just be adamant you want social services involved. Your ultimate aim is to get someone other than you to see the mother and child. You do not necessarily want them referred to social services if another party (such as the GP) becomes involved.

Role Play 3.5 Colleague's Brief

You are Stevie, an experienced receptionist in General Practice and have worked part time for the last 8 years in your current practice. The practice is in a leafy middle class area and there is very little ethnic diversity.

The GP partnership has just started a drug rehabilitation clinic and you had huge reservations when you heard about it, as you "know" that drug users bring trouble. Your opinion is that all drug users are bad people, all break the law and are all dangerous. At the meeting with the practice manager when you were informed about the new clinic, you voiced your opinion, telling them "there will be trouble, mark my words…"

Much to your surprise, over the last 6 weeks since the weekly clinic has been running, there has been no trouble, the patients have always been polite and although you have been anxious on the days the clinic was running, you have been ok.

Today is not a drug clinic day, but one of the patients from yesterday's clinic has just come into reception, intoxicated, demanding to see the GP. The drug rehabilitation GP went on holiday today and is not available. The patient told you that their prescription from yesterday was wrong and they need more methadone. You were very firm and explained to the patient that the GP was not available but they could make an appointment. They refused, swore at you, said they would come back and "sort you out" on another day, then stormed out of the practice.

You are frightened. You immediately call the only doctor in the building who is the new F2. You want to go to speak to them to tell them that the patient should be banned from the surgery and to ask them to call the police.

Insist that you are too traumatised to go back to work and want to go home. You are frightened to leave alone because of their threat and want a taxi (you don't drive). Insist that the practice pays for you. Tell the F2 that you "knew it would be trouble" and you refuse to come back to work until the drug rehabilitation clinic is cancelled.

Continues on the next page …

Additional information

You are unhappy in your job and are actively looking for another job to move to. The practice manager changed a year ago and things have not been the same since. Although you are worried about the drug patients, this seems to be the perfect excuse to go on sick leave with "stress". You know that if you visit your own GP they will sign you off and then you will have a few weeks to look for another job without the hassle of going into work.

Do not tell the GP this unless they probe into your home life and how happy you are at work.

Role Play 3.6 — Colleague's Brief

You are Lee, a community midwife. You had a meeting with the senior partner in the GP surgery yesterday regarding your caseload. Although the meeting went well, you noticed that the partner smelt of alcohol. You tried to make a joke of it during the meeting and asked: "Have you been out for a nice lunch with a beer on the side?". The partner became aggressive with you and told you to "mind your own business", that "the meeting was to discuss patients not his social life".

You completed the meeting and decided to pop in today to check everything was ok. You bumped into the senior partner on the way in and again he smelt of alcohol. You also noticed in his shopping bag was a bottle of vodka. You are now very concerned that he is drinking at work and may even be an alcoholic.

The only other person in the practice is an F2 doctor. You ask to speak to them to discuss the senior partner as you feel something needs to be done urgently. If the F2 asks you, say that you do not feel able to confront the partner. You do not feel that it is your responsibility. Tell the F2 doctor that you think the partner needs reporting to the GMC and should be struck off if he is drinking on the job.

At the beginning of the role play, be apologetic for disturbing them and tell them it is a very awkward situation. Do not tell the doctor straight away what the problem is. Be embarrassed that you have to tell them this. Make the F2 work hard to get the information out of you. Once you have told the F2 about the problem with the partner, become very assertive. Tell the F2 that they need to confront the partner. Tell them that the partner must not see any patients until this matter is cleared up.

If you are not satisfied with the explanation and follow up from the F2, then tell them you are going to report the doctor to the GMC and walk out. If however you are happy with the F2's explanation, then for the rest of the consultation, be supportive. Your main aim is to get someone else to take responsibility of this problem. You do not want to have to talk to anyone else. Once you have told the F2, you feel that your responsibility is over.

Role Play 3.7 Colleague's Brief

You are Xen, a 3rd year medical student on a placement in hospital. For the last 4 weeks you should have attended a tutorial with a junior doctor (F2) but have been unable to make it. You did not call to explain your absence, as you did not think it was necessary. You are attending today but can only stay for 30 minutes and then you will have to leave because you have another "appointment" to attend.

You are a conscientious medical student and usually are very punctual and hardly ever miss any tutorials or lectures.

Over the last 4 weeks you have had a problem. Your husband/wife has broken their leg and after an initial stay in hospital is now relatively house-bound. You have a 2-year-old child whom your husband/wife usually takes to nursery on his/her way to work. You are now the sole carer for this child and are struggling to cope with medical school, revising for your upcoming exams whilst looking after your partner and 2-year-old child. In fact the reason why you need early is really because you need to look after them both; it has nothing to do with an "appointment".

You do not want to admit that you are not coping, as you are worried about getting a bad report. You have heard that some people who have struggled to cope have been given extra time to complete their medical training and you cannot have this happen. You are paying for your medical degree yourself, having already completed a degree and you need to finish in the quickest time possible in order to start earning money. You cannot risk having to repeat a year or take longer to qualify.

When the doctor challenges you about your attendance make excuses but avoid telling the real reason at first. If the doctor asks your opinion on what grade they should give you, tell them "excellent". You normally are an excellent student but have slipped slightly due to personal circumstances.

Only when the doctor says they will have to give you a bad report should you tell them about your problems and then only when they ask specific questions. Do not tell them everything unless the right questions are asked. For example, do not divulge that you are self-funding your medical degree unless they ask about your financial worries.

Role Play 3.8   Colleague's Brief

You are Mr/Mrs Sunar, a lead pharmacist attached to A&E. You are very good at what you do and have worked in the same hospital for many years. You are beginning to get irritated with the relentless changeover of doctors every 6 months and this has been made worse by the new training scheme where the F2 doctors change every 4 months. By the end of their attachment, you feel that you have the doctors prescribing properly with very few mistakes and then the changeover happens and it all starts again.

Today is a bad day. You missed the bus to work this morning and had to drive in. You then got stuck in terrible traffic and were 45 minutes late. When you arrived you found that 4 of your team pharmacists were off sick and so you know this is going to be a very long and very busy day.

You have just received a prescription from A&E requesting penicillin for a gentleman with tonsillitis. In the history that the doctor took on the casualty card, it clearly states that the patient is allergic to penicillin. When you realised it was the F2, you saw red. All of your anger regarding the journey, the relentless change over doctors and the pharmacists being off sick has amalgamated into a rage.

You have asked to see the F2 to teach him a lesson about prescribing. Enter the consultation angry. Shout, saying something like: "You are supposed to be a responsible doctor, you could have killed this man....."

Try to remain standing throughout the scenario. If you are offered a seat, refuse saying that you "do not have time to sit and chat". If the doctor asks you THREE times to sit down, on the third request take a seat and allow some of your anger to subside. Still remain annoyed but be less aggressive.

If the doctor does not repeat the request to sit down then continue to stand and allow your anger to remain fierce.

Explain to the doctor that it is very dangerous to prescribe penicillin to a patient that is allergic and that the patient could have died from a reaction.

Continues on next page

Tell the doctor that you are not there to babysit them and they need to take some responsibility for themselves.

Ask for an explanation as to why the doctor has made the mistake, tell them you are going to report them to their consultant and that you personally will review all of the patients that they have treated over the last couple of weeks to check how many more mistakes have been made.

The way the scenario goes will very much depend on how much the doctor calms you down. If they calm you enough to talk normally then you could use the review of patients as a teaching exercise for the F2, if you remain angry, it can be a treat to get them in trouble with their consultant.

If the doctor asks about you and your personal situation, take the opportunity to offload about the problems you have. If you are standing, be angry and accusative, if you are sitting, confide in the doctor more calmly.

Role Play 3.9 | Colleague's Brief

You are Sister French, a very intelligent ward sister. When you initially left school, you wanted to train to be a doctor, but did not get the A-level grades you needed for medical school and so you trained to be a nurse instead.

You still have the desire to train to be a doctor and have researched the possibility. You have found a University (you choose the city) that will take you as a nurse as long as you do a preclinical year. This would mean a 6-year training course. You have decided that this is definitely what you want to do, but would like to talk to someone about it in more detail. You want to find out what it is really like being a medical student and working as a junior doctor.

The F2 doctor on the ward is very nice and you have decided to sit and talk to them to find out about their experience at medical school. Ask what ever you want but to. You could include the following:

- What is it like having to study for so long?
- How hard is the course?
- How hard are the exams?
- Do they think that you will be accepted as a nurse? You know that some medical students and doctors look down at nurses. Do they think it will be a problem?
- What is the social life like?
- Did they enjoy their training?
- What was the best and worst time they had at medical school?
- When they started work, how difficult was it?
- How tiring is it working long hours?
- How much do they get paid?

Your aim is simply to get facts. If they ask about you, give little information. You are a private person. You are happy and well, you will self-fund the course and plan to work bank shifts as a nurse to pay for it.

Role Play 3.10 | Colleague's Brief

You are Destiny, a practice nurse. You run the immunisation clinic. You have just injected a patient with a flu vaccine and after it had been given, you realised it was out of date. You usually check before you give the vaccine but today you are busy and for some reason forgot.

You are panicking.

You did not tell the patient, initially thinking that it wouldn't matter and so the patient has left the surgery. Initially you thought you would cover it up – after all, who would ever find out? But now you are frightened that something might happen to the patient.

You need to talk to someone and the only other person in the building is an F2 doctor whom you do not know very well. You need to ask them what you should do.

Be very frightened and panicky. Repeatedly say:

- "What happens if the patient dies...?"
- "Oh my goodness, I will be struck off if anyone finds out......"

Be scared.

If the doctor asks, there is a vaccination helpline that the supplying pharmacy runs and that you could call to ask for immediate advice. You have not yet contacted them.

The ideal outcome in this scenario is for the doctor to calm you down and to talk about what happened, to ensure you contact the patient and to initiate a significant event analysis/incident report. They will need to involve the practice manager or a senior partner.

Role Play 3.11 | Colleague's Brief

You are Charlie, a medical staffing officer at a busy hospital. You are responsible for looking after the medical doctors and have been heavily involved in organising the rota. All of the doctors were told at the beginning of their attachment that if they wanted any time off then they should arrange cover amongst themselves.

You specifically told them you did not want to be involved in arranging swaps; you do not have the time. A doctor has asked to see you and will ask you for time off over a weekend that they are due to work nights.

Your attitude is that it is not your responsibility and you have told the doctors that you will not be involved. They should have sorted it out earlier and then one of the other doctors could have swapped with them.

There is no money in the budget for a locum if they ask.

Do not offer solutions, simply deflect any suggestions they have away stating that *"you were told it is your responsibility to make changes and to ensure there is cover".*

If the doctor suggests paying for a locum, then you can engage with them. You would be willing to organise the locum if they offer to sacrifice some of their pay to cover the costs.

If the doctor suggests taking unpaid leave, engage with them, but do not accept this as a solution. The cost of a locum will outweigh the cost of 2 days of their wages and the budget does not have the facility to cope with this.

Ensure at some point you tell the doctor that you will make a note of the weekend in question and if they call in sick, that it will constitute a written warning and their consultant will be involved.

The role play may be very short if the doctor does not try to find a solution. If the conversation feels like it is over, leave. You do not need to stay for the whole 10 minutes.

Role Play 3.12 | Colleague's Brief

You are Hans, an experienced midwife based on labour ward. As part of the routine care of women in labour pethidine (a controlled drug) is offered as pain relief. You are always very careful when using pethidine. You know it is a drug that can be abused and is dangerous if given in the wrong dose.

The rule on labour ward is that 2 midwives check the pethidine, and that it is clearly documented in the controlled drugs book. You always have to check the amount available on opening the locked cupboard, deduct the amount you have used and then recount the amount left available to ensure none is missing.

Over the last 3 shifts, you have noticed a worrying problem. One of the midwives (Frechna) has started using larger doses than normal. Instead of requesting 50mg per patient, she has started taking 100mg.

Today you decided to investigate a little and although she is signing 100mg out of the book, she is only giving the patient 50mg. On the patient's drug chart it states that 50mg is being given. There are no details of the other 50mg being discarded or any entry in the patient notes regarding additional doses later on. You are concerned that Frechna may be stealing the additional pethidine for personal use.

She is currently away from work as she called in sick again today. (Do not tell the doctor this unless they specifically ask).

Facts that you know about Frechna:

- She has just split from her husband.
- Her eldest child has just left to go to university.
- She has 2 other children, one of whom is profoundly autistic.
- She has recently been turning up late for work and has called in sick 2 or 3 times in the last month.
- She always looks tired.
- She has had 3 patient complaints in the last week. Previously she was a highly-sought-after midwife and the patients in antenatal clinic fought to be able to see her.

You do not want to approach the labour ward manager as you know that Frechna is having a hard time and you don't want to make it worse for her. You want to talk about this in confidence to someone to find out what you should do, and to ask for suggestions about how you can approach Frechna without involving anyone else.

Open the scenario by asking the doctor if they are willing to talk in strict confidence. Get them to promise not to tell anyone about what you wish to discuss. If they refuse, keep talking about confidentiality and the need to keep this conversation quiet until they agree to your terms.

Your aim is to get advice from the doctor about how to approach Frechna. Do not agree to go to the labour ward manager or to any other member of staff. If the doctor tells you that they are going to report it, be very disappointed. Try to use emotional blackmail to convince them that they do not need to.

- She's having a really hard time…
- I can sort this out… You don't need to tell anyone else

If they still insist, bargain for some time.

- OK. But give me a couple of days. If I haven't stopped her by then, I promise I will go and report it.
- Give me until the end of today. Let me try to talk to her…

Role Play 3.13 Colleague's Brief

You are a ward nurse and are 2 hours into a 12 hour shift.

You have a terrible headache and sore throat. You think you have tonsillitis as you've suffered from this many times and know that if you attack it with antibiotics early then the illness only lasts for a couple of days.

There is no one to cover the ward if you go off sick and so during your 15-minute break you have decided to run down to A&E to ask one of the doctors to prescribe some antibiotics for you. You are allergic to penicillin. Do not tell the doctor this unless they specifically ask about allergies. You want some erythromycin.

If the doctor tells you to go and see your GP, tell them you cannot leave the ward. If they suggest you register at A&E and then they will see you tell them you do not have time. You are the only qualified member of staff on the ward and you cannot leave.

If they refuse to prescribe for you, leave stating that you "will just have to take them from the drug trolley then".

If the role play finishes early it does not matter.

If the doctor asks to examine you, show them this:

Mani is apyrexial. There are swollen lymph nodes in the neck and the tonsils have an exudate.

This is consistent with tonsillitis.

Role Play 3.14 Colleague's Brief

You are Waleed, an occupational therapist covering general medicine. You have just been to the private ward to arrange a home visit for one of the patients. Mrs Day was admitted 2 weeks ago with a urine infection and is now "medically fit for discharge". She is 82 and, since she has been in bed for 10 days, her mobility has significantly deteriorated.

You and the physiotherapist have been seeing her daily and have arranged for a home visit to ensure that she is safe to be discharged back into her own home. From the work you have done with her in the kitchen, you have strong reservations as to whether she will cope as she lives alone.

You have discussed possible rehabilitation with her and she is keen to proceed as along as it is on the NHS. She cannot afford to continue to pay.

The nurses on the ward tell you that the ambulance has been booked to send her home in 2 hours. You have tried to contact the consultant but cannot reach him. You do not consent to her discharge.

Other information:
You are fed up with doctors undermining your decisions regarding patient discharge. You are a professional in your own right, have completed years of training including a degree, and have many years of experience. Do not tell them this information unless they ask about how you are and how your work is going. You are starting to feel worthless on the ward. Why bother assessing patients for discharge if the doctors do not listen to your advice?

Be adamant that this woman is NOT going home. You forbid it. She is not safe. If the doctor tells you that she's going anyway, tell them that it will be their responsibility if something happens to her. State that you would be willing to stand up in court and blame the doctor who wrote the discharge form. If they tell you to sort it out with the consultant, tell them you are unable to reach them despite several attempts to contact them and that the F2 needs to make the decision.

Your aim is to get the doctor to apologise and to override the consultant's decision.

Role Play 3.15 Colleague's Brief

You are Phil, a receptionist in General Practice. You are good at your job. You always try to be polite and as helpful as you can to the patients, doctors and nurses within the practice.

Your father had an accident 2 weeks ago and is still recovering in hospital. He is now well but has a problem mobilising and so is in a rehabilitation hospital. You are visiting every day after work. You are exhausted.

You came into work this morning and the practice manager asked to see you in their office. They told you that a patient has complained that you were rude to them. The practice manager has implemented a full investigation into the complaint.

You do remember the incident. You were closing the practice door to lock up at 7pm, 2 nights ago. A patient came in and as you were closing the door asked if they could come in and make an appointment for the following week. You told them you were closing and that they could call tomorrow morning to arrange to see someone. They told you it was their "right" to make and appointment, but you refused to let them in as you were already running late (the door is usually locked at 6:45pm) and you needed to get to the rehabilitation hospital to see your dad.

You do not believe you were rude to the gentleman, but since you are so tired you cannot be certain. You don't need this stress and hassle on top of everything else and are almost at breaking point.

You have asked to chat to one of the F2 doctors with whom you get on well. Your aim is to ask them if you are a good receptionist and if they think you are ever rude.

When you enter the scenario, with your body language show that you are tired. Rub your eyes occasionally and sigh. Rest your head on your hand. Close your eyes occasionally.

Be subtle to start with. If the doctor does not pick up on the physical cues, then yawn a couple of times.

Start the conversation by asking:

- I know this is probably a strange thing to ask, but what do you think of my work?
- Am I rude?

Don't tell the doctor initially about either your dad or the complaint. Let them ask you questions. If they show concern about you and your personal life, then tell them why you are worried and why you are so tired.

J Role play practice Discussions

In this section, we have provided explanations and points of discussion for each role play. The section will follow the style of the *Simplified assessment criteria for role play* (page 35).

The scenarios are numbers are follows:

- 1.1 to 1.15: With patient
- 2.1 to 2.15: With relative or carer
- 3.1 to 3.15: With colleague

For each of the first 5 scenarios of each style (i.e. 1.1 to 1.5, 2.1 to 2.5 and 3.1 to 3.5) we have provided very detailed explanations showing what is expected of you during the scenario.

For the remaining 10 scenarios of each style (i.e. 1.6 to 1.15, 2.6 to 2.15 and 3.6 to 3.15), we have provided less detailed explanations, focusing on the areas of role play where specific emphasis is needed. Again, the explanations are based on the 6-point *"Simplified assessment criteria for role play"* on page 35. Though all the areas are potentially important, we have highlighted with asterisks (***) the areas on which you should focus specifically and in which the examiners will be particularly interested.

Getting it right: There is a lot of information in the discussions and you may not have time to cover all of it in your role play. The discussion is there to point out all possible approaches and information that you could get from the scenario. Try rerunning it to see if you can practise other ways of approaching the patient to glean as much information as you can. The more you try and practise, the easier and the more natural it will feel on the day.

Role Play 1.1 | Discussion

1. **Create a safe environment and read the doctor's brief given to you**

   a. **Read, read and read again!**
   The first thing to do is read the brief. Read it and read it again. Did you do that? Did you get halfway through and forget something, which meant that you had to refer back to the brief?

   Next ask yourself: "What do I know from the brief?" You know that the symptom is tiredness and daytime napping. In this case, the brief also tells you that the physical history, examination and routine tests are all normal. It is very common in a scenario of this type to fall into the trap of taking the history again. The brief specifically tells you that this is not necessary.

   Start to think about what could be causing the patient's problem. Don't make assumptions, but start to pinpoint areas from the *Simplified assessment criteria for role play* on page 35 that could be relevant in this case. If you start to think of these before the patient comes in, then you are more likely to ask appropriate questions.

   b. **Move the furniture if you need to and put your watch where you can see it**
   Did you move the furniture?
   Were you sitting too close or too far away from the patient?
   Was it comfortable?

2. **Introduction and active listening**

   a. **Start the conversation sensibly**
   Did you use the patient's name? If not, why not? It was in the brief. You may want to start the scenario by finding out what the patient remembers in order to ensure that your information matches theirs.

   - Hello again Mr/Mrs Edwards, it's nice to see you again. How can I help today?

> - Can you remember what we talked about last time?

By asking this kind of open questions, you will allow the patient to talk, which will allow you to find out exactly why they have come to see you. In this case, the patient wanted to talk about the psychosocial causes of their fatigue, but it may have been that the patient was unhappy with your previous treatments and investigation and wanted another test or referral to a specialist. Do not assume anything.

Do not add any information to the brief unless the patient tells you that information. Just as in real life, the only things we know about our patients are written down or told to us during a consultation. We don't make things up in the hospital/clinic. Don't do it in the role play.

b. **Active listening**
Are you listening, looking and feeling the emotions?
Did you listen and give the patient time to talk?
Did you allow them to tell you why they were there?
If they were quiet, did you encourage them to talk using open questions?
Did you use any silence?
Did you look, listen and feel?
Did you listen to what they were saying?
Did you listen to what they were not saying?
Did you look and see how they behaved?
What was their body language saying?
Did you feel any emotions the patient gave out?
Did you feel any emotions evoked in you?
Were they depressed, angry, nervous or agitated?

c. **What is the patient's expectation?**
Did you ask what the patient wanted?

> - How do you think I can help you today?
> - What are you worried about?
> - Is there anything else you would like to talk about?

3. **Verbal communication**

a. **Explanations of diagnoses and plans of action should be clear and pitched at the correct level**
    In this scenario you have already ruled out a clinical cause for their symptoms. You could have explained this again to the patient, making sure that you used words and terms that they would understand.

> ▪ With all the tests and examinations we have done before, I can't find any physical cause for your symptoms.
> ▪ Do you remember that last time we talked about the fact that there was no evidence of a physical cause for your symptoms?

The differential diagnosis does not really come into play in this scenario.

If you managed to elicit the psychosocial information from the patient, then you will hopefully have decided that the working diagnosis is related to the patient's sick child, lack of sleep, poor support network, unsupportive partner and worries about his/her partner's affair.

As a management plan, there are several approaches:

i. **Support from you, the GP**
    Follow-up appointments, offer of counselling or other help.

ii. **Support from the health visitors for the 4-year-old with cystic fibrosis**
    All children under 5 years of age should be supported by a health visitor when required. If you mentioned this in the role play, the patient may have become very guarded (as per their brief), allowing you to explore their fears of removal of their children by social services. This is an unfounded fear and, as stated in the patient brief, if you were compassionate and allayed the fears of the children being taken away then the patient should have opened up to you and accepted your help. If this didn't happen, why didn't it? What happened to stop a positive resolution?

117

iii. **Support from the family**
You could explore the option of extended family members or friends to help.

iv. **Support from the partner**
Discussing with the patient the amount of support that they could expect from their partner may have allowed the issue of the partner's affair to surface. This in turn may have led to a discussion about how the patient's issues should be discussed with the partner and also about the possible involvement of external agencies and counselling services such as Relate.

b. **Clinical questioning (if appropriate) should show safe practice**
Many people will have headed straight for the safe area of history-taking and clinical questioning. Did you? The brief explicitly states that you do not need to retake a history. It is appropriate to double-check that the symptoms are the same but time wasted on a thorough clinical history will impair your ability to probe into more appropriate avenues.

- Can I just check if anything has changed since we last met?
- How are your symptoms compared to last time we met?

If the patient states that nothing has changed and your brief also states that nothing has changed, move on.

c. **Have you given the patient choice?**
Did you ask the patient if they had any ideas about what they wanted?

- Who would you like me to contact?
- What would you like us to do next?

4. **Non verbal communication**

a. **Your body language**
How was your eye contact?
Are you a floor or ceiling thinker?
Do you think you were too close/too far away from the patient?
Did you notice any irritating habits?

b. **Did you pick up on the patient's body language?**
   Were there any hairy moments?
   Did the patient get upset or angry?
   How did you respond to this?
   Did you feel yourself becoming emotionally involved, angry or irritated?
   What did you do to resolve it?
   What would you do next time?

c. **Was there a hidden agenda?**
   Did you find the hidden agenda?

5. **Relevant psychosocial information**
   This was the main focus for this scenario, but very easily missed if you did not ask the questions. Look at the patient's brief.

   The patient is given clear instructions not to talk about their worries over their partner unless specifically asked. If you have missed the "social" questions, you have missed the whole purpose of this scenario. Can you see how easy it is to lose points? Equally, by asking a few simple questions, it is very easy to get all the information you need from the patient.

Psychological
- How are you coping?
- How is it affecting you?
- How are you sleeping at night?

Financial
- Are you working at the moment?

Social
- Who is with you overnight to help?
- Do you have anyone to talk to?
- Who is around in the daytime to help?

Spiritual
- Who do you confide in?

6. **Checking understanding and close**

   a. **Did you specifically ask if the patient understood?**
      Did you ask? If not, why not? Remember it is not enough to assume they know what is happening. You need to *show* the assessors that you have asked.

   b. **Is there a follow up or next meeting planned?**
      This is very important in this case. Your patient is not coping and has three young children. You need to ensure that the children are safe by involving the health visitor. If you were compassionate, the patient would have agreed to this follow-up. If, for some reason, your patient refused to allow the health visitor to become involved, then ask yourself why.

      The patient's brief was specific, so what happened to make them disagree? Whether they agreed or not, you do have a duty to inform the health visitor if you have any concerns about any child under the age of 5. For any serious concerns (not appropriate in this case), social services, the local paediatrician and the police can also assist.

   c. **Did you finish in 10 minutes?**

Role Play 1.2 | Discussion

1. **Create a safe environment and read the doctor's brief given to you**

   a. **Read, read and read again!**
   The first thing to do is read the brief. Read it and read it again. Did you do that? Did you get halfway through and forget something and have to refer back to the brief?

   Next ask yourself: "What do I know from the brief?"

   You know that the patient attended once with back pain with no significant cause for concern. You know that nothing has changed from the previous history and examination. It is common for us to fall into the trap of the history-taking and, although it is important to double-check the "red flag" signs, you should not spend a large proportion of your time on it as you will lose valuable time.

   Start to think about what could be causing the patient's problem. Don't make assumptions, but start to pinpoint areas from the *Simplified assessment criteria for role play* on page 35 that could be relevant in this case. If you start to think of these before the patient comes in, then you are more likely to ask appropriate questions.

   b. **Move the furniture if you need to and put your watch where you can see it**
   Did you move the furniture?
   Were you sitting too close or too far away from the patient?
   Was it comfortable?

2. **Introduction and active listening**

   a. **Start the conversation sensibly**
   Did you use the patient's name? If not, why not? It was in the brief.

121

You may want to start the scenario by finding out what the patient remembers in order to ensure that your information matches theirs.

- Hello again Mr/Miss Dewen, it's nice to see you again. How can I help today?
- Can you remember what we talked about last time?

By asking this kind of open questions, you will allow the patient to talk, which will allow you to find out exactly why they have come to see you.

In this case, the patient wanted to talk about the psychosocial causes of their back pain, but it may have been that the patient was unhappy with your previous treatments and investigation and wanted another test or referral to a specialist. Do not assume anything.

Do not add any information to the brief unless the patient tells you that information. Just as in real life, the only things we know about our patients are written down or told to us during a consultation. We don't make things up in the hospital/clinic. Don't do it in the role play.

b. What is the patient's expectation?
Did you ask what the patient wanted?

- How do you think I can help you today?
- What are you worried about?
- Is there anything else you would like to talk about?

c. Are you listening, looking and feeling the emotions?
Did you listen and give the patient time to talk? Did you allow them to tell you why they were there?
If they were quiet, did you encourage them to talk using open questions?
Did you use any silence?
Did you look, listen and feel?
Did you listen to what they were saying?
Did you listen to what they were not saying?
Did you look and see how they behaved?

What was their body language saying?
Did you feel any emotions the patient gave out?
Did you feel any emotions evoked in you?
Were they depressed, angry, nervous or agitated?

3. Verbal communication

a. Explanations of diagnoses and plans of action should be clear and pitched at the correct level

After only 2 weeks of pain, which is improving with no sinister signs, your only differential diagnosis is one of musculoskeletal pain. Did you explain this to the patient in a clear way at a level that they understood?

If you managed to elicit the psychosocial information from the patient you will hopefully have decided that the working diagnosis is a stress-related one resulting from a new line manager at work who is "bullying" the patient. If you didn't elicit this, ask yourself why. What else could you have asked to find out? Was it a time issue? Did you spend so much time on retaking the history that you didn't get time to assess the psychosocial aspect of care?

With regard to the management, there are several approaches:

i. Support from you, the GP, in talking through the issues
You can start this in your role play, but often you will need to suggest another appointment. This could be a double appointment.

ii. Support from work
Is there someone at work whom the patient can talk to?
Is there a union representative whom the patient can approach? What about the occupational health department for support? Is there a work counsellor?

iii. Support from the family/ friends
Who can the patient talk to at home?
What friends can the patient rely on?

iv. **Support from the Citizens Advice Bureau (CAB)**
This is a free and confidential service where the patient can get advice regarding a number of matters including employment law, financial support and divorce.

b. **Clinical questioning (if appropriate) should show safe practice**
Many people will have headed straight for the safe area of history-taking and clinical questioning. Did you? The brief explicitly states that the history and physical examination have not changed. It is appropriate to double-check that the symptoms are the same but time wasted on a thorough clinical history will impair your ability to probe into more appropriate avenues.

- Can I just check if anything has changed since we last met?
- How are your symptoms compared to last time we met?

In this type of case, it is also worth checking that there are no red flag signs once again. If the patient states that nothing has changed and your brief also states that nothing has changed, move on.

In this case, things have slightly improved, so you can be further reassured that there is no significant physical problem. Did you ask yourself why the patient presented? If things are improving, why did they want more time off work? If this happens in your role play, ask yourself: "What am I missing?"

If things aren't clear, always go straight to the psychosocial history.

c. **Have you given the patient choice?**
Did you ask the patient if they had any ideas about what they wanted?

- Who would you like me to contact?
- What would you like us to do next?

In this case the patient simply wanted signing off work with a bad back for another month.

124

The Sickness or "Fitness" certificate is the certificate that we sign as doctors and that patients give to their employers justifying their absence from work. It is a legal document and we need to put a diagnosis on the form. In this particular case, signing a patient off work with back pain when this is resolving and they are physically fit for work would be an untruthful statement.

You could compromise with the patient and give them one further week off work for the back problem to resolve completely and ask them to try to resolve the problem at work by talking to the firm.

An alternative would be to sign them off with a stress-related problem if you clinically thought that the patient was significantly affected, again on the understanding that they would approach their work and try to resolve the problem.

4. Non verbal communication

a. Your body language (did you remain calm?)
How was your eye contact?
Are you a floor or ceiling thinker?
Do you think you were too close/too far away from the patient?
Did you notice any irritating habits?

b. Did you pick up on the patient's body language?
Were there any hairy moments?
Did the patient get upset or angry?
How did you respond to this?
Did you feel yourself becoming emotionally involved, angry or irritated?
What did you do to resolve it?
What would you do next time?

c. Was there a hidden agenda?

5. Relevant psychosocial information
This was the main focus for this scenario, but very easily missed if you did not ask the questions. Look again at the patient's brief. The patient was given clear instructions not to tell the doctor about their work worries unless specifically asked. If you have missed the "social" questions, you have missed the whole purpose of this scenario. See

how easy it is to loose points? Equally, by asking a few simple questions, it is very easy to get all the information you need from the patient.

Psychological
- How are you coping?
- How is it affecting you?
- How are you sleeping at night?

Financial
- You have been off work for 2 weeks. How are you coping?

Social
- What are you able to do for yourself?
- Do you feel able to go back to work?

Spiritual
- Who do you confide in?

6. **Checking understanding and close**

   a. **Did you specifically ask if the patient understood?**
   Did you ask? If not, why not? Remember it is not enough to assume they know what is happening. You need to *show* the assessor that you have asked.

   b. **Is there a follow up or next meeting planned?**
   Whatever happened in your scenario, follow-up is important in this case. Review of a patient who is signed off work with a psychological problem is advisable to ensure that some progress is being made. If you resolved the problem in your scenario, it is always worth suggesting they return if they need to at any time for further help. In this case, the offer of a double appointment at the next visit to continue your support would also be invaluable.

   c. **Did you finish in 10 minutes?**

Role Play 1.3 | Discussion

1. **Create a safe environment and read the doctor's brief given to you**

   a. **Read, read and read again!**
      The first thing to do is read the brief. Read it and read it again. Did you do that? Did you get halfway through the scenario and forget something and have to refer back to the brief?

      Next ask yourself: "What do I know from the brief?" The brief in this case is very simple. You know that from the triage information, the patient is concerned that that have a urine infection. It is common for us to fall into the trap of the history-taking as this is where we are most comfortable. Did you move on from the urine infection and find out the patient's "hidden agenda"?

      Remember to start to think about what could be causing the patient's problem. Don't make assumptions, but start to pinpoint areas from the *Simplified assessment criteria for role play on page 35* that could be relevant in this case. If you start to think of these before the patient comes in, then you are more likely to ask appropriate questions.

   b. **Move the furniture if you need to and put your watch where you can see it**
      Did you move the furniture?
      Were you sitting too close or too far away from the patient?
      Was it comfortable?

2. **Introduction and active listening**

   a. **Start the conversation sensibly**
      Did you use the patient's name? If not, why not? It was in the brief. You may want to start the scenario by finding out what the patient remembers in order to ensure that your information matches theirs:

127

> - Hello Miss Little, how can I help today?
> - I understand you have spoken to our nurse triage, can you tell me a little bit about your problem?

By asking this kind of open questions, you will allow the patient to talk, which will allow you to find out exactly why they have come to see you. In this case, the patient wanted to talk about her risk of a sexually transmitted disease and to organise a smear test.

Do not add any information to the brief unless the patient tells you that information. Just as in real life, the only things we know about our patients are written down or told to us during a consultation. We don't make things up in the hospital/clinic. Don't do it in the role play.

b. What is the patient's expectation?
Did you ask what the patient wanted?

> - How do you think I can help you today?
> - What are you worried about?
> - Is there anything else you would like to talk about?

Was there a hidden agenda? In this case the hidden agenda was the important thing to explore. Did you find it?

c. Are you listening, looking and feeling the emotions?
Did you listen and give the patient time to talk?
Did you allow them to tell you why they were there?
If they were quiet, did you encourage them to talk using open questions?
Did you use any silence?
Did you look, listen and feel?
Did you listen to what they were saying?
Did you listen to what they were not saying?
Did you look and see how they behaved?
What was their body language saying?
Did you feel any emotions the patient gave out?
Did you feel any emotions evoked in you?
Were they nervous or agitated?

3. **Verbal communication**

a. **Explanations of diagnoses and plans of action should be clear and pitched at the correct level**
   The first step is to illicit whether the patient has a urine infection (which is covered in the clinical questioning). This patient clearly does not have a urine infection, and your explanation should be clear.

   - From what you've told me, I do not think you have a urine infection. Is there something else on your mind?
   - Was there any other reason you wanted to see me today?

   If you found out about her concerns regarding a sexually transmitted infection (STI) and her wish to have an "urgent" smear test, you should hopefully have explained at an appropriate level the need for urine testing (for Chlamydia), speculum examination with swab testing and blood tests. There is no urgency to perform a smear today (although if you agreed to do the sexual health screen – AFTER the scenario, it only takes 2 minutes extra to do the smear). Some of you will have referred her to a sexual health clinic which is acceptable management, but again your explanation of what will be done should have been clear and at the right level for your patient to understand.

   The main aim should be to explore her fears regarding the smear test, why she has not attended before now (with 3 reminders from the practice) and to explain clearly the association between HPV and cervical cancer.

   With regard to the management, there are several approaches:

   i. **Discuss her concerns and have a follow up appointment for the examination and smear test**

   ii. **Send her to a sexual health clinic**

   iii. **Find out if she has any support.**
       Who can the patient talk to at home?
       Can she confide in a mother, sister or friend whilst waiting for her results?

129

b. Clinical questioning (if appropriate) should show safe practice
Firstly you should have concluded that the risk of a UTI with no symptoms is low and then moved on to "other reasons" for attending. Remember: if things aren't clear you can always go straight to the psychosocial history.

Once you found out about the risk of STIs and the overdue smear, your clinical questioning should then have included a simple sexual health questionnaire:

- Does she have a regular partner?
- How many partners has she had in the last 6 months?
- Does she use contraception?
- Has she has sex with a high risk person (e.g. drug user)?

c. Have you given the patient choice?
Did you ask the patient if they had any ideas about what they wanted?

How do you think we can best help you today?
Would you like me to perform the examination and tests or would you rather go to a sexual health clinic?

4. Non verbal communication

a. Your body language (did you remain calm?)
How was your eye contact?
Are you a floor or ceiling thinker?
Do you think you were too close/too far away from the patient?
Did you notice any irritating habits?

b. Did you pick up on the patient's body language?
Were there any hairy moments?
Did the patient get upset or angry? How did you respond to this?
Did you feel yourself becoming emotionally involved, angry or irritated? What did you do to resolve it? What would you do next time?

c. Was there a hidden agenda?
In this case the whole scenario was based on the hidden agenda.
Did you find it?

5. **Relevant psychosocial information**
   If you got stuck after finding out she had no symptoms consistent with a UTI, hope fully you then went to the psychosocial history, which may have helped you.

Psychological
- How are you?
- Are you worried about anything?
- Is there anything in your mind?

Financial
Not appropriate in this case

Social
- What do you do in your spare time?
- Do you have anyone to talk to?

Spiritual
- Who do you confide in?

6. **Checking understanding and close**

   a. **Did you specifically ask if the patient understood?**
   Did you ask? If not, why not? Remember it is not enough to assume they know what is happening. You need to *show* the assessor that you have asked.

   b. **Is there a follow up or next meeting planned?**
   Whatever happened in your scenario, follow-up is important in this case. If the patient is sent to the sexual health clinic, good practice would be to invite her back for a review to discuss her results and to ensure that she had her smear test performed. If you perform the tests, then you will need to discuss those results with her yourself. Explaining the time scale for results to come through and how the patient will get those results is as important as performing the tests themselves.

   c. **Did you finish in 10 minutes?**

Role Play 1.4 | Discussion

1. **Create a safe environment and read the doctor's brief given to you**

   a. **Read, read and read again!**
   The first thing to do is read the brief. Read it and read it again. Did you do that? Did you get halfway through and forget something and have to refer back to the brief?

   Next ask yourself: "What do I know from the brief?"

   You know very little about the patient whom you are about to see and you have minimal information. You know that Hilary was found unconscious and needed resuscitating. You know there were 2 empty medication bottles and 2 empty bottles of wine. The paramedics told you there was a "suicide note" but they did not bring that with them and so you have not read it. All the information provided points to suicide. Your consultant wants you to ask your patient.

   Start to think about what you are going to say. How are you going to ask? What words will you use? What are the possible reactions? What will you do if the patient cries or shouts?

   What sections and questions from the *Simplified assessment criteria for role play* on page 35 could be relevant in this case? If you start to think of these before the patient comes in, you are more likely to ask the appropriate questions.

   b. **Move the furniture if you need to and put your watch where you can see it**
   Did you move the furniture?
   Were you sitting too close or too far away from the patient?
   Was it comfortable?
   Were there any tissues on the desk?
   Were they close enough for you to reach to give to the patient?
   Did you need to touch the patient to console them?
   Were you close enough to do this comfortably?
   How would you position the room differently next time?

2. Introduction and active listening

a. Start the conversation sensibly

Did you use the patient's name? If not, why not? It was in the brief.

You have only met this patient today and you need to ask difficult questions in the role play.

Did you ask directly about suicide? How long did it take you to ask? What else did you do to assess the patient's mental state? What happened when you mentioned the suicide note? How did it feel having the wrong information? Did you "accuse" Hilary of attempting suicide? Did you believe them when they said they didn't write a suicide note; or did you still believe the paramedic? Remember, do not assume anything. Do not add any information to the brief unless the patient tells you that information. Just as in real life, the only things we know about our patients are written down or told to us during a consultation. We don't make things up in the hospital/clinic. Don't do it in the role play.

b. Are you listening, looking and feeling the emotions?

Hilary has been depressed and is reliant on alcohol. He/she needs support. Did you listen and give the patient time to talk? Did you allow them space to talk? If they were quiet, did you encourage them to talk using open questions?

The patient was instructed in the brief to "switch off" and only come back into the consultation if actively encouraged to do so. Did you notice that they had switched off? What did you do to bring them back in?

When a patient disengages from a consultation, it is usually obvious. In the role play situation, the actor patient will give you big clues that they have switched off. They may look away from you, look to the floor or ceiling. They may hold their head in their hands. Remember to look, listen and feel.

Look and watch your actor patient. Remember that they are trying to help you. If you watch their body language you will know how they are responding. Try it in your own clinical practice over the next few days. Watch the patient. It is amazing how much you learn from their non-verbal communication.

There are always candidates who do not notice that the patient has switched off. Was that you? How long did you carry on talking before noticing? If you did notice, did you use any silence?

If the patient became upset, how did you respond?
What would you do next time?
If your patient was angry, why do you think they were angry?
What did you do or say to ease their fears?

Often, reflecting back a patient's emotion helps to alleviate a difficult situation:

- I can see you are really upset.
- It is ok to be upset.
- I can see that you are angry, can you tell me why?

The other approach is to use silence. Sometimes saying nothing will give the patient the room and space to vent their feelings. Active listening is often all that is required.

An alternative is to ask the patient how you can help alleviate their emotions.

- I can see you are really angry, what can I do to help?
- It is ok to be upset. Can I do anything for you?

c. **What is the patient's expectation?**
   This section is not relevant to this role play.

3. **Verbal communication**

   a. **Explanations of diagnoses and plans of action should be clear and pitched at the correct level**
      Did you choose your words carefully?
      Did you explain to Hilary why you thought it was an attempted suicide?
      Did you explain how serious his/ her collapse was?

134

Did you tell them about the suicide note, the empty alcohol and drug bottles? Did he/she understand why you were contemplating a psychiatric referral?

In terms of a management plan, there are several approaches:

i. **Support Hilary medically**
    You should have picked up on the fact that Hilary has a good relationship with the GP. You could offer to telephone the GP ensuring that they are kept in the loop. Many GPs will contact patients who have has a significant hospital admission such as this and ask them to come into the surgery for a review. This is even more important with possible attempted suicide.

    In this case, even though Hilary says it was not a planned suicide, did you decide to refer to psychiatry anyway? The alcohol and depression may need assessment.

    Someone who is using alcohol in these quantities may need help from an alcohol service locally or by offering the AA (alcoholics anonymous).

ii. **Family support**
    Did you know that Hilary has a sister? Did you ask details about the alleged suicide note? Did you find out Hilary was saying "goodbye" before she went on holiday?

    You could offer to call his/her sister to chat about what had happened to Hilary to ensure they have support on discharge.

b. **Clinical questioning (if appropriate) should show safe practice**
    You may want to know a little about Hilary's behaviour in the preceding days. A simple suicide risk could be undertaken. This would include:

    ▪ Previous suicide attempts
    ▪ Any warnings given to friends or family
    ▪ Mood in the preceding days
    ▪ Family problems
    ▪ Financial problems
    ▪ Work situation

- Was there anyone expected to return or was the suicide performed when Hilary knew they wouldn't be found until it was too late?

c. **Have you given the patient choice?**
Patient choice is important particularly relating to who to talk to and who to inform.

4. **Non verbal communication**

a. **Your body language (did you remain calm?)**
How was your eye contact?
Are you a floor or ceiling thinker?
Do you think you were too close/too far away from the patient?
Did you notice any irritating habits?
If the patient became upset, did you touch them?
Did this feel natural?
What would you do next time?

b. **Did you pick up on the patient's body language?**
Were there any hairy moments?
Did the patient get upset or angry?
How did you respond to this?
Did you feel yourself becoming emotionally involved, angry or irritated? What did you do to resolve it?

c. **Was there a hidden agenda?**

5. **Relevant psychosocial information**
This is very important in a potential suicide attempt.

Psychological
Ask yourself the following questions:
- What state of mind is Hilary in?
- Did you find out that Hilary had been suffering from depression and had consulted the GP?
- Were there any signs of self-harm or attempted suicide?
- How is Hilary now? You can find this out by watching (look, listen and feel), but also by asking "How are you?" or "Are you all right?"

Financial
- Do you have any money worries?

Social
- Do you have any support?
- Can I call anyone for you?
- Who is at home with you?

Spiritual
- Who do you confide in?

6. **Checking understanding and close**

   a. **Did you specifically ask if the patient understood?**
      Did you ask? If not, why not? Did Hilary realise how serious his/her collapse was? Did they understand that they almost died? Remember, it is not enough to assume they know what is happening. You need to show the assessor that you have asked.

   b. **Is there a follow up or next meeting planned?**
      Whatever happened in your scenario, follow-up is important. Make sure that you have articulated this and that the assessor knows your plans for follow up with the GP and or psychiatry.

   c. **Did you finish in 10 minutes?**

Role Play 1.5   Discussion

1. Create a safe environment and read the doctor's brief given to you

a. Read, read and read again!

The first thing to do is read the brief. Read it and read it again. Did you do that? Did you get halfway through and forget something and have to refer back to the brief?

Next ask yourself: "What do I know from the brief?"

You do not know why the patient is attending, but you do have a lot of information about them.

Start to think about what could be causing the patient to attend today. Don't make assumptions, but start to pinpoint areas from the *Simplified assessment criteria for role play* on page 35 that could be relevant in this case. If you start to think of these before the patient comes in, then you are more likely to ask appropriate questions.

b. Move the furniture if you need to and put your watch where you can see it

Did you move the furniture?
Were you sitting too close or too far away from the patient?
Was it comfortable?

2. Introduction and active listening

a. Start the conversation sensibly

Did you use the patient's name? If not, why not? It was in the brief.

You may want to start the scenario by finding out what the patient remembers in order to ensure that your information matches theirs.

- Hello Mr/Mrs Tims it's nice to see you today.
- How can I help you today?

By asking this kind of open questions, you will allow the patient to talk, which will allow you to find out exactly why they have come to see you. In this case it is to get help with their weight loss. Do not assume anything.

Do not add any information to the brief unless the patient tells you that information. Just as in real life, the only things we know about our patients are written down or told to us during a consultation. We don't make things up in the hospital/clinic. Don't do it in the role play.

b. What is the patient's expectation?
Did you ask what the patient wanted?

- How do you think I can help you today?
- What are you worried about?
- Is there anything else you would like to talk about?

Was there a hidden agenda? Did you find out that their father had just died?

c. Are you listening, looking and feeling the emotions?
Did you listen and give the patient time to talk?
Did you allow them to tell you why they were there?
If they were quiet, did you encourage them to talk using open questions?
Did you use any silence?
Did you look, listen and feel?
Did you listen to what they were saying?
Did you listen to what they were not saying?
Did you look and see how they behaved?
What was their body language saying?
Did you feel any emotions the patient gave out?
Did you feel any emotions evoked in you?
Were they depressed, angry, nervous or agitated?

3. Verbal communication

a. Explanations of diagnoses and plans of action should be clear and pitched at the correct level
Talking to someone about weight loss can be very difficult especially as in this case where the patient does not realise what they are doing wrong to make their weight problem worse. It

139

requires a non-judgmental and patient centred approach. You will not complete everything in a single consultation. This is likely to involve the multidisciplinary team (nurses, dieticians) and regular visits to the surgery.

With regard to the management, there are several approaches:

i. **Support from you, the GP in talking through the issues**
What are they doing now and how can you change their behaviour for long term weight loss.

ii. **Support from the family/ friends**
Who can the patient talk to at home?
What friends can the patient rely on?
Is there anyone at home who could go on the diet with them or exercise with them for moral support? It's often easier if the whole family tries to change their behaviour at the same time

iii. **Support from the multidisciplinary team**
Nurses, dieticians

iv. **Support from community diet programmes**
Weightwatchers, Slimming World, etc. There is now good evidence that these "community" groups produce better weight loss than many conventional medical programmes.

b. **Clinical questioning (if appropriate) should show safe practice**
There is no significant clinical questioning that is appropriate in this case. It is all about their diet and way of life.

To be thorough you could ask about their hypertension, diabetes and sleep apnoea and how they are coping with their medication but you should not waste time on this.

Remember; if things aren't clear, always go straight to the psychosocial history.

c. **Have you given the patient choice?**
Did you ask the patient if they had any ideas about what they wanted?

- Who would you like to see next time, me or the nurse?
- What would you like us to do next?
- How can I best help you to achieve the weight loss you want?

4. **Non verbal communication**

   a. **Your body language (did you remain calm?)**
      How was your eye contact?
      Are you a floor or ceiling thinker?
      Do you think you were too close/too far away from the patient?
      Did you notice any irritating habits?

   b. **Did you pick up on the patient's body language?**
      Were there any hairy moments?
      Did the patient get upset or angry?
      How did you respond to this?
      Did you feel yourself becoming emotionally involved, angry or irritated? What did you do to resolve it? What would you do next time?

   c. **Was there a hidden agenda?**
      The only thing of significance was that the patient's dad had just died and that was the reason to spur in the weight loss. Did you find this out?

5. **Relevant psychosocial information**

   Psychological
   - How are you?
   - How is your weight affecting you?
   - How are you sleeping at night?
   - Do you ever get comments about your weight from others?
   - How are you coping after your father's death?

   Financial
   - How do you afford to buy all of the food that you eat?

   Social
   - What exercise do you do?
   - Howe often would you go out eat?
   - Do you eat alone or with others?

Spiritual
- Who do you confide in?
- Who do you usually ask for help?

6. Checking understanding and close

a. Did you specifically ask if the patient understood?
Did you ask? If not, why not? Remember it is not enough to assume they know what is happening. You need to *show* the assessor that you have asked.

b. Is there a follow up or next meeting planned?
Whatever happened in your scenario, follow-up is important in this case. As a patient looses weight, their medication need will change as their diseases improve with the changes made. You will need to see this patient to monitor their diseases.

Weight loss is very difficult, even for the motivated. Giving follow up and support is essential with you the GP, the nurses and /or the dieticians.

c. Did you finish in 10 minutes?

By this stage you will hopefully have gained a good idea of how to conduct your role plays and how to use the assessment criteria to determine whether you are on the right path.

Through practice and by reading the detailed explanations provided for the first 5 role plays you will have noticed that there is a large degree of commonality between role plays. For the next 10 role plays involving patients, we have provided more concise explanations and shown only the areas which are of particular focus – marked with asterisks (***).

This is not to say that the other areas are not important. They are! But they are just part of the standard routine that you should follow and therefore do not warrant specific explanations.

Role Play 1.6 | Discussion

1. **Create a safe environment and read the doctor's brief given to you**

    a. **Read, read and read again!**

    b. **Move the furniture if you need to and put your watch where you can see it**

2. **Introduction and active listening**

    a. **Start the conversation sensibly**

    b. **What is the patient's expectation?**

    c. **Are you listening, looking and feeling the emotions?**

3. **(***) Verbal communication**

    a. **Explanations of diagnoses and plans of action should be clear and pitched at the correct level**
        This is the single most important aspect of this scenario. You need to use clear verbal communication so that the patient can understand you. Did you use alternative ways of communicating? Did you write things down?

    b. **Clinical questioning (if appropriate) should show safe practice**

    c. **Have you given the patient choice?**

4. **(***) Non verbal communication**
    Did you use non-verbal communication with this patient to engage? Did you try gestures, drawing pictures, using patient leaflets, writing things down?

a. **Your body language (did you remain calm?)**
It can be very frustrating when talking to someone who is hard of hearing. Did you get irritated?

b. **Did you pick up on the patient's body language?**

c. **Was there a hidden agenda?**

5. **Psychosocial influences**
Psychological, social, financial, spiritual

6. **Checking understanding and close**

a. **Did you specifically ask if the patient understood?**

b. **Is there a follow up or next meeting planned?**

c. **Did you finish in 10 minutes?**

Role Play 1.7 Discussion

1. **Create a safe environment and read the doctor's brief given to you**

    a. **Read, read and read again!**

    b. **Move the furniture if you need to and put your watch where you can see it**

2. **(***) Introduction and active listening**

    a. **Start the conversation sensibly**

    b. **What is the patient's expectation?**
        Did you accept their decision to die and to stop treatment?

    c. **Are you listening, looking and feeling the emotions?**
        Did you pick up on the patient's anxiety? Did you realise they had a fear of dying in pain?

3. **(***) Verbal communication**

    a. **Explanations of diagnoses and plans of action should be clear and pitched at the correct level**

    b. **Clinical questioning (if appropriate) should show safe practice**
        Did you check for an element of depression?
        Did you check the patient's capacity?

    c. **Have you given the patient choice?**
        Do they want to die at home or in a hospice?
        How do they want you to be involved?

4. **Non verbal communication**

    a. **Your body language (did you remain calm?)**

145

    b.   **Did you pick up on the patient's body language?**

    c.   **Was there a hidden agenda?**

5. **Psychosocial influences**
Psychological, social, financial, spiritual

6. **Checking understanding and close**

    a.   **Did you specifically ask if the patient understood?**

    b.   **Is there a follow up or next meeting planned?**

    c.   **Did you finish in 10 minutes?**

Role Play 1.8 Discussion

1. **Create a safe environment and read the doctor's brief given to you**

    a. **Read, read and read again!**

    b. **Move the furniture if you need to and put your watch where you can see it**

2. **(***) Introduction and active listening**

    a. **Start the conversation sensibly**

    b. **What is the patient's expectation?**
        Did you realise they just wanted company?

    c. **Are you listening, looking and feeling the emotions?**
        If the patient got upset, did you recognise it and calm them down?

3. **Verbal communication**

    a. **Explanations of diagnoses and plans of action should be clear and pitched at the correct level**

    b. **Clinical questioning (if appropriate) should show safe practice**

    c. **Have you given the patient choice?**

4. **Non verbal communication**

    a. **Your body language (did you remain calm?)**

    b. **Did you pick up on the patient's body language?**

    c. **Was there a hidden agenda?**

5. **(***) Psychosocial influences**
Psychological, social, financial, spiritual

The psychosocial history is the most important part of this history.
- Did you find out that they lived alone?
- Did you find out they were lonely?
- Did you work out what they liked to do?
- Did you offer them alternative ways to spend their time?
Volunteering, day centres, hobbies, etc.?

6. **Checking understanding and close**

a. **Did you specifically ask if the patient understood?**

b. **Is there a follow up or next meeting planned?**

c. **Did you finish in 10 minutes?**

Role Play 1.9   Discussion

1. **Create a safe environment and read the doctor's brief given to you**

   a. **Read, read and read again!**
   Did you think about Gillick competence before the patient came into the room?

   b. **Move the furniture if you need to and put your watch where you can see it**

2. **(***) Introduction and active listening**

   a. **Start the conversation sensibly**

   b. **What is the patient's expectation?**
   Did you work out that the patient was determined to get the pill?

   c. **Are you listening, looking and feeling the emotions?**

3. **(***) Verbal communication**

   a. **Explanations of diagnoses and plans of action should be clear and pitched at the correct level**
   The main thing about this scenario is to *show* the examiners that you are testing the "competence" of this 15 year old. Were you clear in your explanation of what taking the pill involves? Did you check her capacity adequately? Did you ask her to involve a responsible adult?

   b. **Clinical questioning (if appropriate) should show safe practice**
   Did you ensure that this girl was safe? It is essential to ensure that any child (under the age of consent i.e. 16) is safe when prescribing the oral contraceptive pill. Did you ask who her partner was? Did you ensure that there was not a child protection issue?

   c. **Have you given the patient choice?**
   Did you offer other types of contraception?

4. **Non verbal communication**

   a. **Your body language (did you remain calm?)**

   b. **Did you pick up on the patient's body language?**

   c. **Was there a hidden agenda?**

5. **Psychosocial influences**
   Psychological, social, financial, spiritual

6. **Checking understanding and close**

   a. **Did you specifically ask if the patient understood?**

   b. **Is there a follow up or next meeting planned?**

   c. **Did you finish in 10 minutes?**

Role Play 1.10 Discussion

1. **(***) Create a safe environment and read the doctor's brief given to you**

   a. **Read, read and read again!**
   Did you think about Gillick competence before the patient came into the room?

   b. **Move the furniture if you need to and put your watch where you can see it**

2. **(***) Introduction and active listening**

   a. **Start the conversation sensibly**

   b. **What is the patient's expectation?**
   Did you realise that the patient only wanted to meet you and see how honest you were?

   c. **Are you listening, looking and feeling the emotions?**

3. **(***) Verbal communication**

   a. **Explanations of diagnoses and plans of action should be clear and pitched at the correct level**
   Were you honest? Did you admit that you did not know anything about this disease?

   b. **Clinical questioning (if appropriate) should show safe practice**

   c. **Have you given the patient choice?**
   Did you allow the patient the choice of not seeing the nurse? Did you offer an alternative?

4. **Non verbal communication**

   a. **Your body language (did you remain calm?)**

   b. **Did you pick up on the patient's body language?**

   c. **Was there a hidden agenda?**

5. **(***) Psychosocial influences**
   Psychological, social, financial, spiritual

   Did you find out about the patient's brothers death and its influence on them?

6. **Checking understanding and close**

   a. **Did you specifically ask if the patient understood?**

   b. **Is there a follow up or next meeting planned?**

   c. **Did you finish in 10 minutes?**

Role Play 1.11 | Discussion

1. **Create a safe environment and read the doctor's brief given to you**

   a. **Read, read and read again!**

   b. **Move the furniture if you need to and put your watch where you can see it**

2. **(***) Introduction and active listening**

   a. **Start the conversation sensibly**

   b. **What is the patient's expectation?**
   Did you realise that the patient wanted support, not stronger pain killers?

   c. **Are you listening, looking and feeling the emotions?**

3. **(***) Verbal communication**

   a. **Explanations of diagnoses and plans of action should be clear and pitched at the correct level**
   Were you clear?

   b. **Clinical questioning (if appropriate) should show safe practice**
   Did you get stuck on the pain relief? Many people fall into the trap of taking a clinical history as this is where we feel "safe". Remember, if things don't seem right, go straight to the psychosocial history!

   c. **Have you given the patient choice?**
   Did you offer options for help, such as hospice care, social services? Did you offer to contact the palliative care team? Did you offer just to listen?

4. **Non verbal communication**

    a. **Your body language (did you remain calm?)**

    b. **Did you pick up on the patient's body language?**
        Did you notice that the patient was "worried"?

    c. **Was there a hidden agenda?**
        Did you find the hidden agenda? Did you realise that this was not a scenario about stronger medication?

5. **(***) Psychosocial influences**
    Psychological, social, financial, spiritual

    Don't ever forget the psychosocial history. This was the most important section in this role play. If you didn't ask about home and how they were coping then you have missed the whole point of the scenario.

6. **Checking understanding and close**

    a. **Did you specifically ask if the patient understood?**

    b. **Is there a follow up or next meeting planned?**

    c. **Did you finish in 10 minutes?**

Role Play 1.12 Discussion

1. **Create a safe environment and read the doctor's brief given to you**

   a. **Read, read and read again!**

   b. **Move the furniture if you need to and put your watch where you can see it**

2. **(***) Introduction and active listening**

   a. **Start the conversation sensibly**

   b. **What is the patient's expectation?**
   Did you realise they just wanted to talk?

   c. **Are you listening, looking and feeling the emotions?**
   Did the patient stop talking to you? Did you pick up on it straight away?

3. **(***) Verbal communication**

   a. **Explanations of diagnoses and plans of action should be clear and pitched at the correct level**

   b. **Clinical questioning (if appropriate) should show safe practice**

   c. **Have you given the patient choice?**
   Remember as long as your patient has capacity, whether to use conventional or alternative medicine is their decision to make. We must not influence patient decisions based on our own personal beliefs.

4. **(***) Non verbal communication**

   a. **Your body language (did you remain calm?)**

b. Did you pick up on the patient's body language?
Did they stop talking and become more aloof or withdrawn?
Did you notice?
What did you do to reengage with the patient?

c. Was there a hidden agenda?
Did you find the hidden agenda?
Did you realise that this was not a scenario about stronger medication?

5. **(***) Psychosocial influences**
Psychological, social, financial, spiritual

Did you ask? Did you realise they were unhappy with the poor control of their psoriasis?

6. **Checking understanding and close**

   a. Did you specifically ask if the patient understood?

   b. Is there a follow up or next meeting planned?

   c. Did you finish in 10 minutes?

Role Play 1.13 | Discussion

1. **Create a safe environment and read the doctor's brief given to you**

   a. **Read, read and read again!**

   b. **Move the furniture if you need to and put your watch where you can see it**

2. **(***) Introduction and active listening**

   a. **Start the conversation sensibly**

   b. **What is the patient's expectation?**
      Did you realise they just wanted an extra top up of their drug?

   c. **Are you listening, looking and feeling the emotions?**
      Did you fall for their emotional blackmail? Did you give in and go against your partner's advice written in the notes?

3. **(***) Verbal communication**

   a. **Explanations of diagnoses and plans of action should be clear and pitched at the correct level**
      Were you clear in your refusal to give any extra methadone?

   b. **Clinical questioning (if appropriate) should show safe practice**

   c. **Have you given the patient choice?**

4. **(***) Non verbal communication**

   a. **Your body language (did you remain calm?)**
      This is a difficult scenario. Did you remain calm even through the anger and tears of your patient?

157

    b. Did you pick up on the patient's body language?
       Did they stop talking and become more aloof or withdrawn?
       Did you notice?
       What did you do to reengage with the patient?

    c. Was there a hidden agenda?
       Did you realise they were lying about being mugged?

5. Psychosocial influences
Psychological, social, financial, spiritual

6. Checking understanding and close

    a. Did you specifically ask if the patient understood?

    b. Is there a follow up or next meeting planned?

    c. Did you finish in 10 minutes?

Role Play 1.14 | Discussion

1. **Create a safe environment and read the doctor's brief given to you**

    a. **Read, read and read again!**

    b. **Move the furniture if you need to and put your watch where you can see it**

2. **(***) Introduction and active listening**

    a. **Start the conversation sensibly**

    b. **What is the patient's expectation?**
        Did you realise the patient just wanted 1-2 tablets for tonight?

    c. **Are you listening, looking and feeling the emotions?**

3. **(***) Verbal communication**

    a. **Explanations of diagnoses and plans of action should be clear and pitched at the correct level**
        Were you clear in your refusal to give any extra methadone?

    b. **Clinical questioning (if appropriate) should show safe practice**
        If you did any clinical questioning in this scenario, you should have checked for depression and possible suicidal intent.

    c. **Have you given the patient choice?**

4. **Non verbal communication**

    a. **Your body language (did you remain calm?)**

    b. **Did you pick up on the patient's body language?**

    c. **Was there a hidden agenda?**

5. **(***) Psychosocial influences**
   Psychological, social, financial, spiritual

   Did you ask? Did you find out about their partner in intensive care? Remember do not forget the psychosocial history; it is often the most important part of the scenario!

6. **Checking understanding and close**

   a. **Did you specifically ask if the patient understood?**

   b. **Is there a follow up or next meeting planned?**

   c. **Did you finish in 10 minutes?**

Role Play 1.15 | Discussion

1. **Create a safe environment and read the doctor's brief given to you**

   a. **Read, read and read again!**

   b. **Move the furniture if you need to and put your watch where you can see it**

2. **(***) Introduction and active listening**

   a. **Start the conversation sensibly**

   b. **What is the patient's expectation?**

   c. **Are you listening, looking and feeling the emotions?**
   Did you realise the patient was frightened about a diagnosis of cancer?

3. **(***) Verbal communication**

   a. **Explanations of diagnoses and plans of action should be clear and pitched at the correct level**
   Did you break the bad news and tell the patient that they have cancer? Did you use the word "cancer?" Was it clear what the diagnosis is?

   b. **Clinical questioning (if appropriate) should show safe practice**

   c. **Have you given the patient choice?**
   Did you ask if the patient wanted to know what their diagnosis was?

4. **Non verbal communication**

    a. **Your body language (did you remain calm?)**

    b. **Did you pick up on the patient's body language?**
        Did you see that the patient was frightened?
        If you told them the diagnosis, did you see that they were
        shocked?

    c. **Was there a hidden agenda?**

5. **(***) Psychosocial influences**
    Psychological, social, financial, spiritual

    Did you find out they had no family support?

6. **(***) Checking understanding and close**

    a. **Did you specifically ask if the actor understood?**
        It is imperative to check that the patient understood what you told
        them.

    b. **Is there a follow up or next meeting planned?**
        Whenever you have broken bad news, you must offer a follow up
        appointment. In this case you know the patient is going to the
        hospital tomorrow. You could follow this up with a telephone call
        or another appointment.

    c. **Did you finish in 10 minutes?**

Role Play 2.1 Discussion

1. **Create a safe environment and read the doctor's brief given to you**

   a. **Read, read and read again!**
   The first thing to do is read the brief. Read it and read it again. Did you do that? Did you get halfway through and forget something and have to refer back to the brief?

   Next ask yourself: "What do I know from the brief"? You know nothing about the relative in front of you, but you know a lot about their family setup and, as it turns out, about the main reason for the consultation since you have previously seen their daughter. This raises a confidentiality issue as Ellen is entitled to complete confidentiality. You should not tell the parent anything about your consultation with Ellen, and some people would say that you should not even acknowledge that Ellen has visited the surgery to see you previously.

   Start to think about why the relative is presenting. It may not be related to the additional information. Don't make assumptions but start to pinpoint areas from the *Summary of proposed assessment criteria for role play* (p.35) that could be relevant in this case. If you start to think of these before the patient comes in, you are more likely to ask the appropriate questions.

   b. **Move the furniture if you need to and put your watch where you can see it**
   Did you move the furniture?
   Were you sitting too close or too far away from the patient?
   Was it comfortable?

2. **Introduction and active listening**

   a. **Start the conversation sensibly**
   Did you use the relative's name? If not, why not? It was in the brief.

You have never met this person before and so starting the consultation with a general open question would be most appropriate.

- Hello Mr/Mrs Gregory. How can I help?
- We've not met before, I'm Dr __. What can I do for you today?

By asking such open questions, you are allowing the relative to talk, thereby helping to ensure that you find out exactly why they have come to see you. In this case, the parent is initially seeking information about his/her daughter's health and help for the daughter's anorexia.

As stated above, confidentiality is the key here and it is important that you explain to Mr/Mrs Gregory that you are unable to give them the information that they want. The manner in which you do this will significantly affect the way the scenario is played out by the actor relative. Go back and read the patient's brief again. If you do this part of the consultation well, the actor relative will continue to engage. If you are blunt or do not offer any other suggestions, then the actor relative is primed to make things difficult for you.

One way of dealing with this opening is by not initially refusing to give any information but continuing to ask more open questions.

- You must be very worried.
- Let's start by working out how this is affecting you rather than concentrating on what Ellen has said.
- What are your biggest fears?

Remember not to assume anything. Do not add any information to the brief unless the actor tells you that information. Just as in real life, the only things we know about our patients is written down or told to us during a consultation. We don't make things up in the hospital/clinic. Don't do it in the role play.

This is particularly important in this scenario as the doctor's brief states that Ellen had said that her sister was dying from leukaemia. The relative's brief explains that the sister is in remission having completed her treatment. If you had disclosed information about Ellen or had assumed that all the information from her was correct without listening to the relative in front of you, problems may have arisen. Did this happen to you? What would you do differently next time?

b. **What is the relative's expectation?**
Did you ask what the relative wanted?

- How do you think I can help you today?
- What are you worried about?
- Is there anything else you would like to talk about?
- Was there a hidden agenda?

c. **Are you listening, looking and feeling the emotions?**
Did you listen and give the patient time to talk?
Did you allow them to tell you why they were there?
If they were quiet, did you encourage them to talk using open questions?
Did you use any silence?
Did you look, listen and feel?
Did you listen to what they were saying?
Did you listen to what they were not saying?
Did you look and see how they behaved?
What was their body language saying?
Did you feel any emotions the patient gave out?
Did you feel any emotions evoked in you?
Were they depressed, angry, nervous or agitated?
If the relative stormed out of the room, why did they? What provoked that reaction? How would you ensure that this did not happen in the future?
If the relative became upset, how did you respond? What would you do next time?

3. **Verbal communication**

a. **Explanations of diagnoses and plans of action should be clear and pitched at the correct level**
It is important to try to explain what anorexia is and ensure that Mr/Mrs Gregory knows that there are multiple agencies that can help; but at the present time, while Ellen has capacity, we cannot force any treatment onto her.

If you managed to elicit the psychosocial information from the relative, you will hopefully have realised that Mr/Mrs Gregory is struggling to cope and needs help. If you didn't elicit this, ask yourself why. What else could you have asked to find out?

As a management plan there are several approaches:

i. **Support for Mr/Mrs Gregory**
    The relative is distressed and needs ongoing support. You, the GP, are in a perfect position to provide continuity of care. Offer an appointment just for them in the next week and make sure that they know that there is support for them. It is very easy in this scenario to concentrate on the daughter and not offer mum/dad any support. Did you fall into this trap? What could you do next time to ensure this doesn't happen?

ii. **Support for the daughter**
    The daughter clearly needs following up. She has missed appointments and now, with the added concerns of the parent, it appears that Ellen's problems could be more serious than they first appeared. Without breaching confidentiality, you need to support the parent and reassure them that you will offer the daughter an appointment. This can be done in many ways, including:

    ▪ Getting Mr/Mrs Gregory to talk to Ellen and ask her to come to the surgery either on her own or as a joint appointment with her parent.

    ▪ Offering to write to or call Ellen to request that she visits the surgery. You do not need to tell the parent that this will be a follow-up appointment.

b. **Clinical questioning (if appropriate) should show safe practice**
    There is clinical history to take in this case. You might want to ask a little more about the laxatives and change in behaviour of the daughter to help next time you see Ellen.

c. **Have you given the patient choice?**
Did you ask the patient if they had any ideas about what they wanted?

- What would you like us to do next?
- How do you think I can help you and Ellen?

4. Non verbal communication

a. **Your body language (did you remain calm?)**
How was your eye contact?
Are you a floor or ceiling thinker?
Do you think you were too close/too far away from the patient?
Did you notice any irritating habits?
If the relative became upset, did you touch them?
Did this feel natural?
What would you do next time?

b. **Did you pick up on the patient's body language?**
Were there any hairy moments?
Did the patient get upset or angry?
How did you respond to this?
Did you feel that you were becoming emotionally involved, angry or irritated?
What did you do to resolve it?
What would you do next time?

c. **Was there a hidden agenda?**

5. Psychosocial influences
Psychological, social, financial, spiritual

One of the significant factors in this role play is that Mr/Mrs Gregory is not coping. Did you work that out? Did you ask?

Psychological
- How are you coping?
- How is it affecting you?
- How are you sleeping at night?

Financial
- How are you coping having an extra person living with you?

Mr/Mrs Gregory does not know about the daughter's debts. Did you divulge this information? If so, why did you?

Social
- Do you have any support?
- Are you able to get any time for yourself?
- What do you do in your spare time?"

Spiritual
- Who do you confide in?

6. **Checking understanding and close**

   a. **Did you specifically ask if the relative understood?**
      Did you ask? If not, why not?
      Do they really know what anorexia is?

      Remember it is not enough to assume they know what is happening. You need to show the assessor that you have asked.

   b. **Is there a follow up or next meeting planned?**
      Whatever happens in your scenario, follow-up is important in this case both for Mr/Mrs Gregory and for Ellen. Make sure that you have articulated this and that the assessor knows your plans.

   c. **Did you finish in 10 minutes?**

Role Play 2.2 | Discussion

1. **Create a safe environment and read the doctor's brief given to you**

   a. **Read, read and read again!**
   The first thing to do is read the brief. Read it and read it again. Did you do that? Did you get halfway through and forget something and have to refer back to the brief?

   Next ask yourself: "What do I know from the brief?"

   You know that you are the only doctor available to talk to the parent of Gianni. You know that your consultant has been involved with the care of the child and has diagnosed a behavioural problem causing school avoidance. You know that this is improving with a behaviour programme. You know that one parent (the main carer, who is not present today) is happy with the care that has been provided.

   From the brief, the main carer has warned you that the estranged "weekend" parent is coming to see you and wants a CT scan for Gianni. You know that their worry is one of a brain tumour.

   You also know that they want to see the consultant.

   Start to think about why this parent is coming to see you. What has made them come now, after the child has been discharged?

   What potential difficulties might arise during this scenario?

   What sections and questions from the *Summary of proposed assessment criteria for role play* (p.35) could be relevant in this case? If you start to think of these before the relative comes in, you are more likely to ask the appropriate questions.

   b. **Move the furniture if you need to and put your watch where you can see it**
   Did you move the furniture? Were you sitting too close or too far away from the relative? Was it comfortable?

2. Introduction and active listening

a. Start the conversation sensibly
Did you use the relative's name? If not, why not? It was in the brief.

You have never met this person before and so starting the consultation with a general open question would be most appropriate.

- Hello Mr/Mrs Evans. How can I help?
- We've not met before, I'm Dr _____. What can I do for you today?

By asking such open questions you allow the relative to talk, ensuring that you find out exactly why they have come to see you. In this case it is for a specific demand. Mr/Mrs Evans is angry and wants a CT scan for his/her child. One way of dealing with an angry person who is making demands is by acknowledging their anger and continuing to ask open questions.

- You are obviously very worried about Gianni.
- What are your biggest fears /worries?

If the relative keeps asking for the CT scan, then acknowledging this without agreeing to it will allow you to move the conversation forward.

- You've said you think Gianni needs a CT scan. Before we talk about that, can I ask you some other questions?
- You would obviously like Gianni to have a CT scan. Can I ask why you would like that?

Remember, do not assume anything. Do not add any information to the brief unless the actor tells you that information. Just as in real life, the only things we know about our patients are written down or told to us during a consultation. We don't make things up in the hospital/clinic. Don't do it in the role play.

It is important in this scenario to work out exactly what this parent knows. This is easy to find out by asking the right questions.

- Do you know why Gianni was referred to us?
- Can you tell me what you know already about Gianni's care?

The other issue that may be raised at the beginning of the consultation is the relative's request to talk to the consultant. This can be difficult to deal with if you are a junior doctor; but being honest and offering an apology is always the best start.

- I'm sorry, Mr/Mrs Evans. The Consultant is not in the hospital today.
  I am Dr _____. I work very closely with the Consultant and have been involved in your son's care.
- I'm sorry. Unfortunately, the Consultant is unavailable. I could offer to book you an appointment with him later in the week if you would like, but perhaps I can help in some way?

Offering an appointment with the consultant shows that you are being open and that the Consultant is willing to talk to Mr/Mrs Evans. If you were clear and compassionate, the relative should have calmed down a little by now. Did they? If they remained angry, why do you think this was? What could you have done differently to alleviate their concerns and help calm them down? What would you do differently next time?

b. **What is the relative's expectation?**
   Did you listen and give the relative time to talk?
   Did you allow them to tell you why they were there?
   If they were quiet, did you encourage them to talk using open questions? Did you use any silence?

How did you respond to the anger? Often, when our patients or their relatives are angry, we meet that anger by talking too much and trying to talk over them. If you remain silent and actively listen, they will rapidly run out of steam, which will make the consultation easier. Have you ever tried to have a heated discussion or argument with someone who refuses to be drawn into it? How quickly did you give up?
Did you look, listen and feel?
Did you listen to what they were saying?
Did you listen to what they were not saying?

Did you look and see how they behaved?
What was their body language saying?
Did you feel any emotions the patient gave out?
Did you feel any emotions evoked in you?
Did the anger make you feel angry, intimidated or anxious?
How did you respond?
What would you do next time?

c. **Are you listening, looking and feeling the emotions?**
You probably did not need to ask what the relative wanted as they demanded the CT scan. Did you explore why they wanted it?

- What do you expect the CT scan to show?
- How do you think that the CT scan will help Gianni?

3. **Verbal communication**

a. **Explanations of diagnoses and plans of action should be clear and pitched at the correct level**
It is important to try to explain that the current working diagnosis for Gianni is related to a pure behavioural problem, that he has been fully assessed by the team including the consultant and that, with his current management, he appears to be improving. You could enquire about possible causes for his behaviour problem but be careful not to apportion blame.

You need to reassure that if there were any concerns about his symptoms pointing to something more sinister then he would have been investigated. He is not deteriorating and appears to be getting better. There are no symptoms suggesting an underlying pathology.

The main management is to ensure that Mr/Mrs Evans is happy with your explanation. If you discovered that their friend died recently from a brain tumour you could explore issues relating to their grieving process. They are clearly upset about their friend's death, which is influencing their reactions to their son's problems. Offering a support service for Mr/Mrs Evans to explore these feeling of grief may help. This can include their own GP or support networks such as Cruse Bereavement Care.

It is important to acknowledge the family difficulties and suggest ways of talking to both parents together. You could offer a joint appointment with you, or with the Consultant on their return, with both parents to explore the concerns further. It may be that their relationship is good enough for them to sit down and talk together either alone or with Gianni's GP.

b. **Clinical questioning (if appropriate) should show safe practice**
You may want to briefly cover the behavioural symptoms that Gianni expresses and ask about fits, faints and funny turns, although this will have been covered in consultation with Gianni.

c. **Have you given the relative choice?**
This has been covered above, but you could ask the patient what they want to happen next.

4. **Non verbal communication**

a. **Your body language (did you remain calm?)**
How was your eye contact? Are you a floor or ceiling thinker?
Do you think you were too close/too far away from the patient?
Did you notice any irritating habits?
If the relative became upset, did you touch them? Did this feel natural? What would you do next time?
If the relative was aggressive, did you find yourself moving away? How did you cope? Did your nerves or anxiety show to the observer or to the patient?

b. **Did you pick up on the relative's body language?**
Were there any hairy moments? Did the relative get upset or angry? How did you respond to this?
Did you feel yourself becoming emotionally involved, angry or irritated? What did you do to resolve it? What would you do next time?

c. **Was there a hidden agenda?**
There is a significant psychosocial component to this role play. Mr/Mrs Evans is scared that their son has a brain tumour. They have just seen their best friend die from this condition and assume

that all personality changes are due to the same cause. Did you find this out? If not, why not?

5. Psychosocial influences
Psychological, social, financial, spiritual

Psychological
- How is Gianni's behaviour affecting you?
- How are you coping with it?

Financial
This is not really important in this case although the relative may offer to go privately. This may allow you to ask how they would be able to afford private health care.

Social
- Do you have any support?
- Are you able to share your worries with anyone?

Spiritual
- Who do you confide in?

6. Checking understanding and close

a. Did you specifically ask if the relative understood?
Did you ask? If not, why not? Do they really understand why you were not concerned about a brain tumour? Did they want to ask any other questions? It is not enough to assume they know what is happening. You need to show the assessor that you asked.

b. Is there a follow up or next meeting planned?
Whatever happened in your scenario, follow-up is important both to ensure that all the parent's concerns regarding their son have been resolved, but also regarding their grief for their friend. Subsequent appointments with the GP, you or the consultant could also address the family dynamics and possible cause for behavioural change in Gianni. Offering bereavement support using the appropriate resources is also important in this case.

c. Did you finish in 10 minutes?

Role Play 2.3 Discussion

1. **Create a safe environment and read the doctor's brief given to you**

    a. **Read, read and read again!**
        The first thing to do is read the brief. Read it and read it again. Did you do that? Did you get halfway through and forget something and have to refer back to the brief?

        Next ask yourself: "What do I know from the brief"?

        You know you have permission to talk to the carer. You know that Hildi has dementia and has deteriorated through out the last year. You also know that there is a specialist team involved with Hildi's care (the memory team) and so you have a wider multidisciplinary team to ask for help if needed.

        Start to think about why the carer has asked to see you. It may not be related to the additional information. Don't make assumptions but start to pinpoint areas from the *Summary of proposed assessment criteria for role play* (p.35) that could be relevant in this case. If you start to think of these before the actor comes in, you are more likely to ask the appropriate questions.

    b. **Move the furniture if you need to and put your watch where you can see it**
        Did you move the furniture?
        Were you sitting too close or too far away from the carer?
        Was it comfortable?

2. **Introduction and active listening**

    a. **Start the conversation sensibly**
        Did you use the carer's name?
        If not, why not? It was in the brief.
        You have never met this person before and so starting the consultation with a general open question would be most appropriate.

175

> - Hello Eddie. How can I help?
> - We've not met before, I'm Dr _____. What can I do for you today?

By asking such open questions you are allowing the carer to talk, thereby helping to ensure that you find out exactly why they have come to see you.

b. What is the carer's expectation?
Did you ask what the carer wanted?

> - How do you think I can help you today?
> - What are you worried about?
> - Is there anything else you would like to talk about?
> - Was there a hidden agenda?

Did you realise that Eddie wanted you to take responsibility for Hildi's move out of the nursing home?

c. Are you listening, looking and feeling the emotions?
Did you listen and give the carer time to talk?
Did you allow them to tell you why they were there?
If they were quiet, did you encourage them to talk using open questions?
Did you use any silence?
Did you look, listen and feel?
Did you listen to what they were saying?
Did you listen to what they were not saying?
Did you look and see how they behaved?
What was their body language saying?
Did you feel any emotions the patient gave out?
Did you feel any emotions evoked in you?
Were they depressed, angry, nervous or agitated?
If the patient became upset, how did you respond? What would you do next time?

3. **Verbal communication**

a. **Explanations of diagnoses and plans of action should be clear and pitched at the correct level**
It is important in this scenario to explain that although you are happy to help Eddie, it is not your sole decision to move Hildi out of the care home. You will need much more information from Hildi, the care home, the memory team and then the social services team will need to be involved to make a formal assessment of Hildi. This is not something that can be decided today.

As a management plan there are several approaches:

   i. Listen to Eddie's concerns. He/she is in a very difficult situation and needs your support.
   ii. Offer to go and see Hildi to make an assessment.
   iii. Offer to talk to the memory team to get up to date information on her dementia.
   iv. Offer to talk to the staff to educate them about dementia and how much extra support patient's need as their disease progresses.
   v. Offer to talk to the relatives.
   vi. Involve social services to make a formal assessment. This is the part that is likely to help Eddie the most. If you refer Hildi to social services and they make the decision to move Hildi, then Eddie has achieved her aim, but without upsetting the staff or the relatives.

b. **Clinical questioning (if appropriate) should show safe practice**
There is clinical history to take in this case. You might want to ask a little more about Hildi's behaviour and how the staff are coping with the changes.

c. **Have you given the patient choice?**
Did you ask the carer if they had any ideas about what they wanted?

   ▪ What would you like us to do next?
   ▪ How do you think I can help you?

177

4. Non verbal communication

a. Your body language (did you remain calm?)
How was your eye contact?
Are you a floor or ceiling thinker?
Do you think you were too close/too far away from the carer?
Did you notice any irritating habits?
If the carer became upset, did you touch them?
Did this feel natural?
What would you do next time?

b. Did you pick up on the patient's body language?
Were there any hairy moments?
Did the carer get upset or angry?
How did you respond to this?
Did you feel that you were becoming emotionally involved, angry or irritated?
What did you do to resolve it?
What would you do next time?

c. Was there a hidden agenda?

5. Psychosocial influences
Did you ask?

Psychological
- How are you coping?
- How is it affecting you?

Financial
- Is the extra care needed for Hildi putting added pressure on the care home budget?

Social
- Have you thought about day centres for Hildi?
- Have you involved social services?

Spiritual
- Who do you confide in?

6. Checking understanding and close

a. Did you specifically ask if the carer understood?

Did you ask? If not, why not? Did they know what the next step is going to be? Remember it is not enough to assume they know what is happening. You need to show the assessor that you have asked.

b. Is there a follow up or next meeting planned?

Whatever happens in your scenario, follow-up is important. It is likely that you have offered to see the patient and discuss her care with the rest of the team. You will need to arrange to talk to Eddie again to update her.

c. Did you finish in 10 minutes?

Role Play 2.4 | Discussion

1. Create a safe environment and read the doctor's brief given to you

a. Read, read and read again!

The first thing to do is read the brief. Read it and read it again. Did you do that? Did you get halfway through and forget something and have to refer back to the brief?

Next ask yourself: "What do I know from the brief"? You know all about Bob's prostate cancer and have discussed it with him. You also know that he does not want his family to know about his cancer. That is his choice and you have no right to break his confidentiality.

Start to think about why the wife is presenting. It may not be related to the additional information. Don't make assumptions but start to pinpoint areas from the *Summary of proposed assessment criteria for role play* (p. 35) that could be relevant in this case. If you start to think of these before the patient comes in, you are more likely to ask the appropriate questions.

b. Move the furniture if you need to and put your watch where you can see it

Did you move the furniture?
Were you sitting too close or too far away from the relative?
Was it comfortable?

2. Introduction and active listening

a. Start the conversation sensibly

Did you use the relative's name?
If not, why not? It was in the brief.
Starting the consultation with a general open question would be appropriate.

- Hello Mrs Pain. How can I help?
- I'm Dr _____. What can I do for you today?

180

By asking such open questions, you are allowing the relative to talk, thereby helping to ensure that you find out exactly why they have come to see you. In this case, the relative is desperate for confirmation that her husband has cancer.

As stated above, confidentiality is the key here and it is important that you explain to Mrs Pain that you are unable to give them the information that they want.

Did you break confidentiality and fall for the lie that the relative told you? Even if a relative tells you they "know" something, you still cannot pass confidential patient information on to them. One way of dealing with this opening is by not initially refusing to give any information but continuing to ask more open questions.

- You must be very worried.
- I know you love your husband, what has he said?
- What are your biggest fears?

Remember not to assume anything. Do not add any information to the brief unless the patient tells you that information. Just as in real life, the only things we know about our patients are written down or told to us during a consultation. We don't make things up in the hospital/clinic. Don't do it in the role play.

b. **What is the relative's expectation?**
Did you ask what the relative wanted?

- How do you think I can help you today?
- What are you worried about?
- Is there anything else you would like to talk about?

c. **Are you listening, looking and feeling the emotions?**
Did you listen and give the relative time to talk?
Did you allow them to tell you why they were there?
If they were quiet, did you encourage them to talk using open questions?
Did you use any silence?
Did you look, listen and feel?
Did you listen to what they were saying?
Did you listen to what they were not saying?

Did you look and see how they behaved?
What was their body language saying?
Did you feel any emotions the patient gave out?
Did you feel any emotions evoked in you?
Were they depressed, angry, nervous or agitated?
If the relative became upset, how did you respond? What would you do next time?

3. Verbal communication

a. Explanations of diagnoses and plans of action should be clear and pitched at the correct level

It is important to try to explain confidentiality clearly to Mrs Pain. Simply refusing to engage with her and tell her anything is going to make her even more worried and possibly angry or upset. Did you manage to explain that as a doctor you can not divulge any information about your patient even to their wife? Did you explain it was against the "medical law" that you work under and you could get in to trouble?

If you managed to elicit the psychosocial information from the patient, you will hopefully have realised that Mrs Pain is frightened for her husband and needs help. If you didn't elicit this, ask yourself why. What else could you have asked to find out?

As a management plan there are several approaches:

i. Support for Mrs Pain

Mrs Pain needs your support. She too is your patient and even though you cannot tell her anything about her husband, you still need to support her through what is going to be a very difficult time – especially if her husband's disease progresses and he dies. You must try to maintain a good doctor patient relationship with her

ii. Offer to meet with her and her husband together

One way of getting round a difficult situation like this is to offer to meet both patients involved to discuss the problem and their worries. Even though Mr Pain does not want his wife to know at the moment, he may in the future decide to tell her and he will definitely need her support if his disease progresses. You could offer to talk to him and ask him if he was willing to meet with his wife present.

You will need to ask Mrs Pain if she consents to you telling her husband that she has been to see you. If she does, during your conversation with Mr Pain, you can make it clear that Mrs Pain knows something is wrong and it would help her to talk about his disease openly.

b. Clinical questioning (if appropriate) should show safe practice
You could ask a little about the symptoms Mrs Pain has witnessed.

c. Have you given the relative choice?
Did you ask the relative what they wanted?

- ▪   What would you like us to do next?
- ▪   How do you think I can help you and Mr Pain?

4. Non verbal communication

a. Your body language (did you remain calm?)
How was your eye contact?
Are you a floor or ceiling thinker?
Do you think you were too close/too far away from the relative?
Did you notice any irritating habits?
If the relative became upset, did you touch them?
Did this feel natural?
What would you do next time?

b. Did you pick up on the relative's body language?
Were there any hairy moments?
Did the relative get upset or angry?
How did you respond to this?
Did you feel that you were becoming emotionally involved, angry or irritated? What did you do to resolve it? What would you do next time?

c. Was there a hidden agenda?

183

5. **Psychosocial influences**

   One of the significant factors in this role play is that Mrs Pain is frightened about her husband having cancer. Did you ask?

   Psychological
   - How are you coping?
   - How is it affecting you?
   - How are you sleeping at night?

   Financial
   - Is Mr Pain's illness having an impact on you financially? Is he going to work?

   Social
   - Do you have any support?
   - Are you able to get any time for yourself?
   - What do you do in your spare time?

   Spiritual
   - Who do you confide in?

6. **Checking understanding and close**

   a. **Did you specifically ask if the relative understood?**
      Did you ask? If not, why not? Do they know what the next steps are going to be? Remember it is not enough to assume they know what is happening. You need to show the assessor that you have asked.

   b. **Is there a follow up or next meeting planned?**
      Whatever happens in your scenario, follow-up is important in this case. Mrs Pain is going to need your support just as much as Mr Pain. Make sure that you have articulated this and that the assessor knows your plans.

   c. **Did you finish in 10 minutes?**

Role Play 2.5 Discussion

1. Create a safe environment and read the doctor's brief given to you

a. Read, read and read again!
The first thing to do is read the brief. Read it and read it again. Did you do that? Did you get halfway through and forget something and have to refer back to the brief?

Next ask yourself: "What do I know from the brief"?

You know that you are about to see the next of kin but do not know if that is a wife, brother or child. You do not know the next of kin's name.

You do know however that the person you are about to meet has just found out their relative has died and is likely to be upset. Prepare yourself for this. Expect tears. Expect anger. Expect the mute patient who says nothing as they are in shock. This is what happens in real life.

Don't make assumptions but start to pinpoint areas from the *Summary of proposed assessment criteria for role play* (p. 35) that could be relevant in this case. If you start to think of these before you go in, you are more likely to ask the appropriate questions.

b. Move the furniture if you need to and put your watch where you can see it
Did you move the furniture?
Were you sitting too close or too far away from the relative?
Was it comfortable?

2. Introduction and active listening

a. Start the conversation sensibly
Did you ask the relative for their name? If not, why not?
You have never met this person before and so starting the consultation with a general open statement would be most appropriate.

- Hello, I'm doctor __. My consultant has asked me to come to speak to you.
- We've not met before, I'm Dr___.
- Before we start, I just want to make sure I'm talking to the right person. Can I ask what your name is?

It is also a good idea to ask the person what relationship they have to Mr Simmons to ensure you are talking to the correct person.

- Can I ask how you are related to Mr Simmons?
- Is it correct that you are his next of kin?

You need to be very careful at the start of this role play and gauge the relative's emotional state. Ask how they are feeling, ask if they understand what has happened and ask if they have any questions for you.

Remember not to assume anything. Do not add any information to the brief unless the patient tells you that information. Just as in real life, the only things we know about our patients is written down or told to us during a consultation. We don't make things up in the hospital/clinic. Don't do it in the role play.

b.   What is the relative's expectation?
The relative was expecting you to tell them that you were ready to turn off the ventilator. Did you realise?
They were expecting the consultant to come to talk to them. Did you manage to avoid a confrontation?
Did you apologise?

c.   Are you listening, looking and feeling the emotions?
Did you listen and give the relative time to talk?
Did you allow them to tell you why they were there?
If they were quiet, did you encourage them to talk using open questions?
Did you use any silence?
Did you look, listen and feel?
Did you listen to what they were saying?
Did you listen to what they were not saying?
Did you look and see how they behaved?

186

What was their body language saying?
Did you feel any emotions the patient gave out?
Did you feel any emotions evoked in you?
Were they depressed, angry, nervous or agitated?
If the relative stormed out of the room, why did they? What provoked that reaction? How would you ensure that this did not happen in the future?
If the relative became upset, how did you respond? What would you do next time?

3. Verbal communication

a. Explanations of diagnoses and plans of action should be clear and pitched at the correct level

It is important to explain what organ donation is and to ask very clearly if they agree. Did you manage to clearly explain that Mr Simmons carried a donor card and it was therefore his wish to donate his organs? Did you offer to get the transplant team down to talk to them?

b. Clinical questioning (if appropriate) should show safe practice
Not appropriate in this case.

c. Have you given the relative choice?
Did you ask the relative if they had any ideas about what they wanted?

- Would you like to talk to your family about this?
- Would you like to talk to the transplant team about this?

4. Non verbal communication

a. Your body language (did you remain calm?)
How was your eye contact?
Are you a floor or ceiling thinker?
Do you think you were too close/too far away from the relative?
Did you notice any irritating habits?
If the relative became upset, did you touch them?
Did this feel natural?
What would you do next time?

    b. Did you pick up on the relative's body language?
       Were there any hairy moments?
       Did the relative get upset or angry?
       How did you respond to this?
       Did you feel that you were becoming emotionally involved, angry or irritated?
       What did you do to resolve it?
       What would you do next time?

    c. Was there a hidden agenda?

5. Relevant psychosocial information

<u>Psychological</u>
- How are you?
- It must be a real shock for you...

<u>Financial</u>
- Not appropriate at this stage of the consultation

<u>Social</u>
- Do you have any support?
- Is there anyone here who can come and sit with us?
- Is there anyone you want me to call?

<u>Spiritual</u>
- Who do you confide in?
- Are you religious? Would you like me to call the hospital chaplain to come to see you?

6. Checking understanding and close

    a. Did you specifically ask if the relative understood?
       Did you ask? If not, why not?
       Do they know what organ donation involves?

       Remember it is not enough to assume they know what is happening. You need to show the assessor that you have asked.

b. Is there a follow up or next meeting planned?
It is unlikely that you got the relative to agree to organ donation during the scenario. You therefore needed to plan to talk to the relative again.

Did you suggest coming back in a few minutes to talk once they had had some tome to think about it?

Did you suggest sending your consultant or the transplant team in to talk to them?

c. Did you finish in 10 minutes?

By this stage you will hopefully have gained a good idea of how to conduct your role plays and how to use the assessment criteria to determine whether you are on the right path.

Through practice and by reading the detailed explanations provided for the first 5 role plays you will have noticed that there is a large degree of commonality between role plays. For the next 10 role plays involving relatives and carers, we have provided more concise explanations and shown only the areas which are of particular focus – marked with asterisks (***).

This is not to say that the other areas are not important. They are! But they are just part of the standard routine that you should follow and therefore do not warrant specific explanations.

Role Play 2.6   Discussion

1. **Create a safe environment and read the doctor's brief given to you**

   a. **Read, read and read again!**

   b. **Move the furniture if you need to and put your watch where you can see it**

2. **(***) Introduction and active listening**

   a. **Start the conversation sensibly**
   You were not told in the brief who the relative was. Did you ask about their relationship with Mrs Singh? If not, why not?

   b. **What is the relative's expectation?**
   Did you realise that Mrs Singh was not going to go home, no matter what you said?

   c. **Are you listening, looking and feeling the emotions?**

3. **(***) Verbal communication**

   a. **Explanations of diagnoses and plans of action should be clear and pitched at the correct level**

   b. **Clinical questioning (if appropriate) should show safe practice**

   c. **Have you given the relative choice?**
   Did you offer alternatives? Carer at home? A care home? Rehabilitation? Day hospital?

4. **(***) Non verbal communication**

   a. **Your body language (did you remain calm?)**

b. **Did you pick up on the relative's body language?**
How difficult did you find the silences? Did you try to talk all the time to fill the silence?
Did you feel that the relative was giving you any information?
Remember to use the silence. Leave it long enough for the patient/relative to fill the silence…

c. **Was there a hidden agenda?**

5. **(***)Psychosocial influences**
Psychological, social, financial, spiritual

Did you ask? If not, why not?
Did you realise that, financially, Jo is struggling as he/she had to take time off work? You could have asked:

- How has it affected you, with your mum being in hospital?
- Have you managed to get to work ok?

Socially, did you realise that there was a family pressure to bring Mrs Singh home? Did you ask about the impact on Jo?

6. **(***) Checking understanding and close**

a. **Did you specifically ask if the relative understood?**

b. **Is there a follow up or next meeting planned?**
How are you going to resolve this? Did you agree to tell Mr Singh that it was your idea to keep Mrs Singh in hospital? Are you happy to lie to him to protect Jo?
Did you offer to meet with Mr Singh and Jo together to talk about it?

c. **Did you finish in 10 minutes?**

Role Play 2.7   Discussion

1. **(***) Create a safe environment and read the doctor's brief given to you**

   a. **Read, read and read again!**
      Did you assume this was a case of abuse even before seeing Asia? If so why? You need to keep an open mind when seeing patients. Always have a high index of suspicion with regard to child protection issues but wait to make your own judgement before calling social services!

   b. **Move the furniture if you need to and put your watch where you can see it**

2. **(***) Introduction and active listening**

   a. **Start the conversation sensibly**
      A good way of opening would be to say:

      - Hello Asia. How are you? Is Thomas not with you today?

   b. **What is the relative's expectation?**
      Did the relative get what she wanted? Did you sign the form and then she left? Did you manage to talk to her about Thomas at all?

   c. **Are you listening, looking and feeling the emotions?**

3. **(***) Verbal communication**

   a. **Explanations of diagnoses and plans of action should be clear and pitched at the correct level**
      Did you manage to explain that social services always try to keep the child with the parents?

   b. **Clinical questioning (if appropriate) should show safe practice**
      Did you ask about Thomas' bruise and how he got it? Did you ask to see Thomas himself?

c. **Have you given the relative choice?**
If you talked about social services referral did you give the relative a choice?

- You could bring Thomas in to see me later or I may have to involve social services.
- Would you be willing to let me see Thomas and to talk to him?

4. **Non verbal communication**

a. **Your body language (did you remain calm?)**

b. **Did you pick up on the relative's body language?**

c. **Was there a hidden agenda?**

5. **(***) Psychosocial influences**
Psychological, social, financial, spiritual

Did you find out about Thomas' dad? Did you find out that Asia was struggling to cope especially now she had injured her ankle?

6. **Checking understanding and close**

a. **Did you specifically ask if the relative understood?**

b. **Is there a follow up or next meeting planned?**
It is important in this scenario to see Thomas and examine him yourself. Did you get mum to agree to bring him in? If not did you tell her you would have to call social services?

c. **Did you finish in 10 minutes?**

Role Play 2.8 Discussion

1. **(***) Create a safe environment and read the doctor's brief given to you**

    a. **Read, read and read again!**
        Did you assume this was going to be a complaint? If so, did it turn into one? Read the actor relative's brief. The aim was for reassurance and support.

    b. **Move the furniture if you need to and put your watch where you can see it**

2. **(***) Introduction and active listening**

    a. **Start the conversation sensibly**

    b. **What is the relative's expectation?**
        Did you realise they wanted reassurance. Did you give the antibiotics? One way of getting round the problem of giving antibiotics to someone who does not need them now is to issue a "delayed script". Tell Steph you will prescribe the antibiotics but not to get them from the pharmacist today. Advise them to wait and see if they get worse over the next 48 hours. They can then pick up the prescription if the want to. Often, people who know they can get antibiotics "if required" don't actually use them.

    c. **Are you listening, looking and feeling the emotions?**

3. **(***) Verbal communication**

    a. **Explanations of diagnoses and plans of action should be clear and pitched at the correct level**
        Were you clear with your explanation of viral illnesses?

b. **Clinical questioning (if appropriate) should show safe practice**
There is a clinical history to take here but Steph has no other symptoms than sneezing a few times. You know from the brief that clinical examination is normal.

c. **Have you given the relative choice?**
Did you offer then antibiotics? Did you offer a delayed prescription? Did you offer to see them again if they got worse?

4. **(***) Non verbal communication**

a. **Your body language (did you remain calm?)**

b. **Did you pick up on the relative's body language?**
Did you realise how upset the relative was. Did you work out he/she was blaming him/herself?

c. **Was there a hidden agenda?**
Did you realise they were scared?

5. **(***) Psychosocial influences**
Psychological, social, financial, spiritual

Did you ask? Did you work out that Steph was blaming him/herself?

6. **(***) Checking understanding and close**

a. **Did you specifically ask if the relative understood?**

b. **Is there a follow up or next meeting planned?**
Steph needs support. His/her sister has just died unexpectedly. He/she is worried that they too will die. Even a follow up telephone call will often help with recently bereaved patients.

c. **Did you finish in 10 minutes?**

Role Play 2.9 Discussion

1. **(***) Create a safe environment and read the doctor's brief given to you**

   a. **Read, read and read again!**
   Did you have any idea that this was going to be about confidentiality and "Gillick competence"? Look back at your brief. Did you notice the daughter was 14 and had been treated for Chlamydia?

   b. **Move the furniture if you need to and put your watch where you can see it**

2. **(***) Introduction and active listening**

   a. **Start the conversation sensibly**

   b. **What is the relative's expectation?**

   c. **Are you listening, looking and feeling the emotions?**
   Did you feel the anger? What do you do to dissipate it? Did you win Mr/Mrs Kahn over by the end?

3. **(***) Verbal communication**

   a. **Explanations of diagnoses and plans of action should be clear and pitched at the correct level**
   Did you explain clearly about Gillick competence and confidentiality? Did the relative understand?

   b. **Clinical questioning (if appropriate) should show safe practice**

   c. **Have you given the relative choice?**

4. **Non verbal communication**

   a. **Your body language (did you remain calm?)**
      Did you manage to remain calm and in control even with Mr/Ms Kahn's anger?

   b. **Did you pick up on the relative's body language?**

   c. **Was there a hidden agenda?**

5. **(***) Psychosocial influences**
   Psychological, social, financial, spiritual

   Why is Mr/Mrs Kahn so upset and angry? Did you ask about the family dynamics? Did you ask about religious influences?

6. **(***) Checking understanding and close**

   a. **Did you specifically ask if the relative understood?**
      It is imperative to check that the patient understood what you told them. If you did and Mr/Mrs Kahn was happy, then you will have avoided a complaint.

   b. **Is there a follow up or next meeting planned?**
      You could offer to see Manji and Mr/Mrs Kahn together to talk about it.

   c. **Did you finish in 10 minutes?**

Role Play 2.10 Discussion

1. **Create a safe environment and read the doctor's brief given to you**

    a. **Read, read and read again!**
    b. **Move the furniture if you need to and put your watch where you can see it**

2. **(***) Introduction and active listening**

    a. **Start the conversation sensibly**
        Did you check who the carer was? Did you get her name? By knowing what job she does will enable you to pitch your level of explanation later at the correct level.

    b. **What is the relative's expectation?**

    c. **Are you listening, looking and feeling the emotions?**

3. **(***) Verbal communication**

    a. **Explanations of diagnoses and plans of action should be clear and pitched at the correct level**
        Did you explain clearly about Nancy's ability to decide for herself? Did you explain about capacity? Did you explain clearly that you will continue to go and see her and to monitor her?

    b. **Clinical questioning (if appropriate) should show safe practice**

    c. **Have you given the carer choice?**
        Did you offer go and see Nancy with the carer present so she could talk to her with you? Did you ask how Anja thought you could help?

4. **Non verbal communication**

    a. **Your body language (did you remain calm?)**

    b. **Did you pick up on the carer's body language?**

    c. **Was there a hidden agenda?**

5. **(***) Psychosocial influences**
    Psychological, social, financial, spiritual

    Did you ask? Did you realise that Anja was fiercely religious and it was this that was influencing her insistence that Nancy should take her medication?

6. **Checking understanding and close**

    a. **Did you specifically ask if the carer understood?**

    b. **Is there a follow up or next meeting planned?**

    c. **Did you finish in 10 minutes?**

Role Play 2.11 | Discussion

1. (***) **Create a safe environment and read the doctor's brief given to you**

    a. **Read, read and read again!**
        There is no information to help you in this brief. Be prepared for anything. Expect the unexpected!

    b. **Move the furniture if you need to and put your watch where you can see it**

2. (***) **Introduction and active listening**

    a. **Start the conversation sensibly**

    b. **What is the relative's expectation?**
        Did you realise this parent wants help and support?

    c. **Are you listening, looking and feeling the emotions?**

3. (***) **Verbal communication**

    a. **Explanations of diagnoses and plans of action should be clear and pitched at the correct level**

    b. **Clinical questioning (if appropriate) should show safe practice**
        There is some history to take here and this boy is likely to need urgent psychiatric assessment and treatment. More information about the amount of cannabis, a basic psychiatric history paying particular attention to suicide risk and safety would be of great value.

    c. **Have you given the relative choice?**
        Did you offer to go and see Asim? Only by assessing him for yourself can you decide if he needs to be seen by the psychiatric team. Did you ask how mum/dad thought you could help them?

4. **Non verbal communication**

   a. **Your body language (did you remain calm?)**

   b. **Did you pick up on the relative's body language?**

   c. **Was there a hidden agenda?**

5. **(***) Psychosocial influences**
   Psychological, social, financial, spiritual

   Did you ask about how this is impacting on the family? Psychiatric illnesses and drug addictions can be very frightening. Does the family feel safe?

   If Asim is a student, did you ask how he is affording to continue with his drug habit? Often parents continue to give their children money even though they know they are going to buy drugs.

6. **(***) Checking understanding and close**

   a. **Did you specifically ask if the relative understood?**

   b. **Is there a follow up or next meeting planned?**
      Asim needs to be seen. Have you arranged that?

   c. **Did you finish in 10 minutes?**

Role Play 2.12 Discussion

1. **Create a safe environment and read the doctor's brief given to you**

   a. **Read, read and read again!**

   b. **Move the furniture if you need to and put your watch where you can see it**

2. **(***) Introduction and active listening**

   a. **Start the conversation sensibly**
   This ladies mother has just died. Did you show empathy and understanding in your greeting?

   - Hello Mrs Pullie, I heard about your mother...... I am so sorry. You must be shocked

   b. **What is the relative's expectation?**
   Did you realise she just wanted to talk to someone?

   c. **Are you listening, looking and feeling the emotions?**
   Did you feel her grief?

3. **(***) Verbal communication**

   a. **Explanations of diagnoses and plans of action should be clear and pitched at the correct level**
   This lady is an ex-nurse. Did you find that out? Did you pitch your explanation at the right level?

   b. **Clinical questioning (if appropriate) should show safe practice**

   c. **Have you given the relative choice?**
   Did you ask her how you could help?

4. **Non verbal communication**

   a. **Your body language (did you remain calm?)**

   b. **Did you pick up on the actor's body language?**

   c. **Was there a hidden agenda?**

5. **(***) Psychosocial influences**
   Psychological, social, financial, spiritual

   This is very important in this case. How is she coping? Who is at home to support her?

   Her mother only died 1 week ago. Have they had the funeral yet? Has she had chance to say goodbye? How is she sleeping?

6. **(***) Checking understanding and close**

   a. **Did you specifically ask if the relative understood?**

   b. **Is there a follow up or next meeting planned?**
      An open follow up would be appropriate here. "Come back and see me anytime you need to talk". "If there is anything I can do, let me know".

   c. **Did you finish in 10 minutes?**

Role Play 2.13 Discussion

1. **Create a safe environment and read the doctor's brief given to you**

   a. **Read, read and read again!**

   b. **Move the furniture if you need to and put your watch where you can see it**

2. **(***) Introduction and active listening**

   a. **Start the conversation sensibly**

   b. **What is the relative's expectation?**
   Did you realise that the relative needs help?

   c. **Are you listening, looking and feeling the emotions?**
   Did you realise how upset he was? That he feels a failure?

3. **(***) Verbal communication**

   a. **Explanations of diagnoses and plans of action should be clear and pitched at the correct level**
   Did you explain carefully that his wife needs to agree to see you, that you cannot force someone to see a doctor?

   b. **Clinical questioning (if appropriate) should show safe practice**
   Did you ask about his wife's symptoms? Did you illicit that she has morning stiffness and pain? Did you illicit the family history?

   c. **Have you given the relative choice?**

4. **Non verbal communication**

   a. **Your body language (did you remain calm?)**

   b. **Did you pick up on the relative's body language?**

c.   **Was there a hidden agenda?**

5.   **(***) Psychosocial influences**
Psychological, social, financial, spiritual

Did you ask? This man needs help. He feels useless. Did you find that out? Did you realise the impact that his wife's illness is having on him?

6.   **(***) Checking understanding and close**

a.   **Did you specifically ask if the relative understood?**

b.   **Is there a follow up or next meeting planned?**
Have you arranged to try to see his wife? Did you agree to the home visit?

c.   **Did you finish in 10 minutes?**

Role Play 2.14 Discussion

1. **(***) Create a safe environment and read the doctor's brief given to you**

   a. **Read, read and read again!**
   Did you prepare yourself for breaking bad news?

   b. **Move the furniture if you need to and put your watch where you can see it**

2. **(***) Introduction and active listening**

   a. **Start the conversation sensibly**
   Did you show empathy when you greeted her?

   - Hello Ann. How are you?" I'm so sorry about Trevor".

   b. **What is the relative's expectation?**

   c. **Are you listening, looking and feeling the emotions?**

3. **(***) Verbal communication**

   a. **Explanations of diagnoses and plans of action should be clear and pitched at the correct level**
   Did you explain clearly that Trevor is going to die soon? Did she understand you?

   b. **Clinical questioning (if appropriate) should show safe practice**

   c. **Have you given the relative choice?**
   Did you ask if Ann wanted any help from you?

4. **(***) Non verbal communication**

    a. **Your body language (did you remain calm?)**
    What did you do when Ann touched your arm? You need to be prepared for patients and relatives to touch you. Were you comfortable? Did you pull away and therefore offend Ann? If you are not comfortable with this, there is no problem, but explain to the patient. "I'm sorry Ann; I didn't mean to pull away from you". "Are you ok?" This way, if you have offended the patient, you will be able to get them back on side. If you ignore the fact the patient has touched you and you ignore the fact that they are offended, the rest of the scenario is likely to be very difficult. Touch is a very therapeutic sense. Are you happy for patients to touch you? Do you ever put your hand on a patient's to comfort them?

    b. **Did you pick up on the relative's body language?**

    c. **Was there a hidden agenda?**

5. **Psychosocial influences**
    Psychological, social, financial, spiritual
    Did you realise that Ann was frightened about being on her own when Trevor died. Did you offer support? Did you ask about family support? Did you ask if she was religious?

6. **(***) Checking understanding and close**

    a. **Did you specifically ask if the relative understood?**

    b. **Is there a follow up or next meeting planned?**
    When are you going to see Trevor again? Often in palliative care cases, we will go and see the patient daily. You could offer to call Ann first thing in the morning to see how the night was. Some GPs still give their mobile number out in cases like this. If something happened overnight, you could offer for her to call you even though you do not cover the on call. If not, have you ensured she has the on call GP number?

    c. **Did you finish in 10 minutes?**

Role Play 2.15 | Discussion

1. **Create a safe environment and read the doctor's brief given to you**

   a. **Read, read and read again!**

   b. **Move the furniture if you need to and put your watch where you can see it**

2. **(***) Introduction and active listening**

   a. **Start the conversation sensibly**

   b. **What is the relative's expectation?**
   Did you realise that he/she does not really want his/her son to go into are, but that they are desperate for help?

   c. **Are you listening, looking and feeling the emotions?**

3. **(***) Verbal communication**

   a. **Explanations of diagnoses and plans of action should be clear and pitched at the correct level**
   Did you offer to refer them to the Health Visitor? (They look after all 0-5 year olds). Did you offer to talk to social services for additional help? Did you think about the private sector and charities? There are often local charities that provide carers or baby sitters, so mum/ dad can get out and get a rest.

   b. **Clinical questioning (if appropriate) should show safe practice**

   c. **Have you given the relative choice?**
   Did you ask how he/she wanted you to help? If they really wanted the child placed into care, why come to you and not go straight to social services?

4. **Non verbal communication**

    a. **Your body language (did you remain calm?)**

    b. **Did you pick up on the relative's body language?**

    c. **Was there a hidden agenda?**

5. **(***) Psychosocial influences**
    Psychological, social, financial, spiritual
    Did you ask?
    Did you realise their partner was away all the time?
    Is there any other family to help?
    Is there a community person/ church/ playgroup helper that they can confide in?
    Do they have a baby sitter?

6. **Checking understanding and close**

    a. **Did you specifically ask if the relative understood?**

    b. **Is there a follow up or next meeting planned?**
        This parent needs support in the long term. Is there a follow up appointment with you, the health visitor or social services set up?

    c. **Did you finish in 10 minutes?**

Role Play 3.1 Discussion

1. **Create a safe environment and read the doctor's brief given to you**

   a. **Read, read and read again!**
   The first thing to do is read the brief. Read it and read it again. Did you do that? Did you get halfway through the scenario and forget something and have to refer back to the brief?

   Next ask yourself: "What do I know from the brief?" The brief in this case is very simple. Your colleague is a medical student who you think is good at what they do and has helped you.

   Start to think about why he/she could want to see you. Don't make assumptions, but start to pinpoint areas from the *Simplified assessment criteria for role play* on page 35 that could be relevant in this case. If you start to think of these before they come in, then you are more likely to ask appropriate questions.

   Remember this is your colleague!

   b. **Move the furniture if you need to and put your watch where you can see it**
   Did you move the furniture?
   Were you sitting too close or too far away from them?
   Was it comfortable?

2. **Introduction and active listening**

   a. **Start the conversation sensibly**
   Did you use Andi's name?
   If not, why not? It was in the brief.
   You may want to start the scenario with an open question.

   Hi Andi, how are you?
   Hi, you asked to talk to me…

   By asking this kind of open questions, you will allow them to talk, which will allow you to find out exactly why they have come to see you. In this case, Andi just wanted a shoulder to cry and some support.

Do not add any information to the brief unless they tells you that information. Just as in real life, the only things we know are written down or told to us during a meeting. We don't make things up in real life. Don't do it in the role play.

b. **What is the colleague's expectation?**
Did you ask what they wanted?

- How do you think I can help you today?
- What are you worried about?
- Is there anything else you would like to talk about?

Was there a hidden agenda? In this case the hidden agenda was for Andi to get support rather than information about who to go to in order to drop out of medicine. Did you realise?

c. **Are you listening, looking and feeling the emotions?**
Did you listen and give them time to talk?
Did you allow them to tell you why they were there?
If they were quiet, did you encourage them to talk using open questions?
Did you use any silence?
Did you look, listen and feel?
Did you listen to what they were saying?
Did you listen to what they were not saying?
Did you look and see how they behaved?
What was their body language saying?
Did you feel any emotions they gave out?
Did you feel any emotions evoked in you?
Were they sad, angry, nervous or agitated?

3. **Verbal communication**

a. **Explanations of diagnoses and plans of action should be clear and pitched at the correct level**
Explanations and discussions with a colleague are as important as with a patient. Did you remember that Andi was a medical student and so you could use medical terminology?

With regard to the plan of action, there are several approaches:

i. **Show empathy and listen.** After all if you read the brief you will realise that Andi just wants help and support.

ii. **Offer to send him home,** so that he/she can be with people to support him/her while you finish the on call.

iii. **Give encouragement.** You think that Andi is a good medical student, did you tell him/ her?

If you had a similar experience during your training or early years in the job, did you share it? Most of us when we experienced an arrest, a death, or a traumatic event for the first time would have been shaken. Some of us hold it in and tell no one, others tell the world. Even if you weren't traumatised by the event that you remember, we all have shaky moments in the early days of working. Share them with Andi. By telling true stories about yourself, the emotions that you experienced will show and you are likely to communicate better, thereby performing better. Try it!

Did you fall into the trap of simply giving advice about how Andi could drop out of the course? If so, you probably missed the psychosocial questions... Try not to in the future.

b. **Clinical questioning (if appropriate) should show safe practice**
You could ask for more detail about the arrest to get a clearer picture of what Andi saw, but this is not essential.

c. **Have you given the colleague choice?**
Did you ask Andi if they had any ideas about what they wanted?

- What would you like to do right now? Go home? Stay on for a while?
- Would you like us to meet up tomorrow to talk about it again?

4. Non verbal communication

a. Your body language (did you remain calm?)
How was your eye contact?
Are you a floor or ceiling thinker?
Do you think you were too close/too far away from Andi?
Did you notice any irritating habits?

b. Did you pick up on the colleague's body language?
Were there any hairy moments?
Did the colleague get upset?
How did you respond to this?
Did you feel yourself becoming emotionally involved, angry or irritated?
What did you do to resolve it?
What would you do next time?

c. Was there a hidden agenda?
Hopefully you realised that Andi just wanted support. Did you?

5. Relevant psychosocial information
The psychosocial section is still important with colleagues.

Psychological
- How are you?
- Are you worried about anything?
- Is there anything in your mind?
- How are you coping with this?

Financial
- What about your course fees? You've already paid tuition fees for 5 years

Social
- Is there anyone at home?
- Do you have anyone to talk to?

Spiritual
- Who do you confide in?

6. Checking understanding and close

a. Did you specifically ask if the colleague understood?

Did you ask? If not, why not? Remember it is not enough to assume they know what is happening. You need to *show* the assessor that you have asked.

b. Is there a follow up or next meeting planned?

Whatever happened in your scenario, follow-up is important in this case. Andi needs support, either from you as his supervisor or from one of your senior colleagues. Even if you don't talk to Andi again, ensuring you offer to call to see if he/she needs any other support is important. We need to ensure that we support our junior colleagues when then need it.

c. Did you finish in 10 minutes?

Role Play 3.2 | Discussion

1. Create a safe environment and read the doctor's brief given to you

a. Read, read and read again!

The first thing to do is read the brief. Read it and read it again. Did you do that? Did you get halfway through the scenario and forget something and have to refer back to the brief?

Next ask yourself: "What do I know from the brief?" The brief in this case is very simple. Your colleague is a nurse who you think is good at what they do. The fact that this nurse is training to be a nurse practitioner is likely to mean that they are experienced and a high quality nurse. Ensure that you remember this during your role play. You need to show that you respect the nurse and ensure you pitch the conversation at the right level.

Start to think about why he/she could want to see you. Don't make assumptions, but start to pinpoint areas from the *Simplified assessment criteria for role play* on page 35 that could be relevant in this case. If you start to think of these before they come in, then you are more likely to ask appropriate questions.

Remember this is your colleague!

b. Move the furniture if you need to and put your watch where you can see it

Did you move the furniture?
Were you sitting too close or too far away from them?
Was it comfortable?

2. Introduction and active listening

a. Start the conversation sensibly

Did you use Denni's name? If not, why not? It was in the brief.

You may want to start the scenario with an open question.

- Hi Denni, how are you?
- Hi, you asked to talk to me...

215

By asking this kind of open questions, you will allow them to talk, which will allow you to find out exactly why they have come to see you. In this case, Denni just wanted help with factual information, with their audit.

Do not add any information to the brief unless they tell you that information. Just as in real life, the only things we know are written down or told to us during a meeting. We don't make things up in real life. Don't do it in the role play.

b. What is the colleague's expectation?
Did you ask what they wanted?

- How do you think I can help you today?
- Is there anything else you would like to talk about?

c. Are you listening, looking and feeling the emotions?
Did you listen and give them time to talk?
Did you allow them to tell you why they were there?
If they were quiet, did you encourage them to talk using open questions?
Did you use any silence?
Did you look, listen and feel?
Did you listen to what they were saying?
Did you listen to what they were not saying?
Did you look and see how they behaved?
What was their body language saying?
Did you feel any emotions they gave out?
Did you feel any emotions evoked in you?

3. Verbal communication

a. Explanations of diagnoses and plans of action should be clear and pitched at the correct level
Explanations and discussions with a colleague are as important as with a patient. Did you remember that Denni was a nurse so you could use medical terminology?

Denni simply wanted help with his/her audit. Did you remember the audit cycle? It can be difficult to explain verbally. Did you try drawing the cycle?

- Identify a subject
- Decide on what criteria you wish to monitor
- Set the "gold standard". (Achieving 100% is unlikely. Ensure standards set are realistic)
- Plan and then execute the monitoring process
- Identify any changes that are needed
- Implement change and plan the re-audit date
- Re-audit to complete the cycle and monitor the changes made to determine if you have reached your "gold standard".

Were you clear in your explanation? Did Denni understand?

Did you have any ideas for an audit in A&E?

Every doctor at the F2 level in the UK should have completed at least one audit. If you couldn't think on your feet during the role play, in the future, use the audit that you have already performed as an example for Denni.

b. **Clinical questioning (if appropriate) should show safe practice**
Not appropriate.

c. **Have you given the colleague choice?**
Did you ask Denni if they had any ideas about what they wanted?

- How do you think I can help?
- Would you like to work with me on my audit?

4. **Non verbal communication**

a. **Your body language (did you remain calm?)**
How was your eye contact?
Are you a floor or ceiling thinker?
Do you think you were too close/too far away from Denni?
Did you notice any irritating habits?

b. **Did you pick up on the colleague's body language?**
Were there any hairy moments?
Did the colleague get upset?
How did you respond to this?

Did you feel yourself becoming emotionally involved, angry or irritated?
What did you do to resolve it?
What would you do next time?

c. **Was there a hidden agenda?**
There is no hidden agenda in this case. If you kept trying to find one, Denni should have told you off. How did you cope with that?

5. **Relevant psychosocial information**
The psychosocial section is still important with colleagues although if you tried to illicit a psychosocial history from Denni, he/she probably told you off. Beware, not every scenario will have a psychosocial element! But you never know until you ask.

Psychological
- How are you?
- Are you worried about anything?
- Is there anything in your mind?

Financial
Although not appropriate in this case, it is important to remember that nurses are not generally paid well and Denni may have to fund his/her nurse practitioner course themselves. It could be adding a strain.

Social
- How are you managing with work and your course?

Spiritual
- Do you have people to talk to?

6. **Checking understanding and close**

a. **Did you specifically ask if the colleague understood?**
Did you ask? If not, why not? Remember it is not enough to assume they know what is happening. You need to *show* the assessor that you have asked. This is imperative in this case. You have to ensure that Denni knows exactly what an audit is before he/she leaves.

b. Is there a follow up or next meeting planned?
Follow up is not necessarily important in this case, but you should
offer to be there is he/she needs more help.

- Give me a call if you have any more questions.
- Let me know if there is anything else I can help with.

c. Did you finish in 10 minutes?

Role Play 3.3   Discussion

1. **Create a safe environment and read the doctor's brief given to you**

   a. **Read, read and read again!**
   The first thing to do is read the brief. Read it and read it again. Did you do that? Did you get halfway through the scenario and forget something and have to refer back to the brief?

   Next ask yourself: "What do I know from the brief?"

   The brief in this case is very simple. Your colleague is a new practice nurse.

   Start to think about why he/she could want to see you. Don't make assumptions, but start to pinpoint areas from the *Simplified assessment criteria for role play* on page 35 that could be relevant in this case. If you start to think of these before they come in, then you are more likely to ask appropriate questions.

   Remember this is your colleague!

   b. **Move the furniture if you need to and put your watch where you can see it**
   Did you move the furniture?
   Were you sitting too close or too far away from them?
   Was it comfortable?

2. **Introduction and active listening**

   a. **Start the conversation sensibly**
   Did you use Alex's name?
   If not, why not? It was in the brief.
   You may want to start the scenario with an open question.

   - Hi Alex, how are you?
   - Hi, you asked to talk to me...

   By asking this kind of open questions, you will allow them to talk, which will allow you to find out exactly why they have come to see

220

you. In this case, Alex needs to get some advice about a difficult colleague.

Do not add any information to the brief unless they tell you that information. Just as in real life, the only things we know are written down or told to us during a meeting. We don't make things up in real life. Don't do it in the role play.

b. **What is the colleague's expectation?**
Did you ask what they wanted?

- How do you think I can help you today?
- What are you worried about?
- Is there anything else you would like to talk about?

There is no hidden agenda in this case.

c. **Are you listening, looking and feeling the emotions?**
Did you listen and give them time to talk?
Did you allow them to tell you why they were there?
If they were quiet, did you encourage them to talk using open questions?
Did you use any silence?
Did you look, listen and feel?
Did you listen to what they were saying?
Did you listen to what they were not saying?
Did you look and see how they behaved?
What was their body language saying?
Did you feel any emotions they gave out?
Did you feel any emotions evoked in you?
Were they sad, angry, nervous or agitated?

3. **Verbal communication**

a. **Explanations of diagnoses and plans of action should be clear and pitched at the correct level**
Explanations and discussions with a colleague are as important as with a patient. Did you remember that Alex was a nurse?

Giving advice to someone about a difficult colleague is one way of testing how YOU would cope in the same situation. How would you approach it? Would you confront the nurse? Would you tell the practice manager? Would you bury your head in the sand and pretend that there was not a problem?

Did you listen to Alex's fears?

Pretending that there isn't a problem in the long term will not work. Alex is bound to start to resent Woo at some point in the future and it may impact on their working relationship and the practice. It is important in small teams such as General Practice to ensure that any problems are dealt with quickly and efficiently, to prevent them festering into something bigger.

Approaching Woo directly is one way (and probably the best way) of approaching the problem with an informal discussion. If Alex was apprehensive about this approach, you could always offer to sit in with them during their discussion. If an informal discussion does not rectify the situation then telling the practice manager would be the next step.

Telling the practice manager directly is an option although it is always best to approach your colleague first if you can. If you are intimidated by your colleague then approaching their line manager (in this case the practice manger) is the second best option. Telling the practice manager, who will then have a meeting with Woo, potentially could make the working relationship between Woo and Alex worse and there will always be the memory that Alex "went behind Woo's back".

Offering to talk to Woo with Alex present is an alternative. The 3 of you having a discussion together is a way of supporting Alex, without involving Woo's line manager. Care should be taken to ensure that Woo does not feel that people are ganging up on her.

Were you clear in your explanations?

b. **Clinical questioning (if appropriate) should show safe practice**
Not appropriate in this case.

c. **Have you given the colleague choice?**
Did you ask Alex if they had any ideas about what they wanted?

- How do you think I can help you?
- There are a few ways of dealing with this, which would you prefer?
- I am happy to be as involved as you want me to be. Tell me how I can help you.

4. Non verbal communication

a. Your body language (did you remain calm?)
How was your eye contact?
Are you a floor or ceiling thinker?
Do you think you were too close/too far away from Alex?
Did you notice any irritating habits?

b. Did you pick up on the colleague's body language?
Were there any hairy moments?
Did the colleague get upset?
How did you respond to this?
Did you feel yourself becoming emotionally involved, angry or irritated?
What did you do to resolve it?
What would you do next time?

c. Was there a hidden agenda?
There was no hidden agenda.

5. Relevant psychosocial information
The psychosocial section is still important with colleagues although in this case less so.

Psychological
- How are you?
- Are you worried about this?
- How are you coping with this?

Financial
- Not appropriate in this case

Social
- Do you have anyone to talk to at home?

Spiritual
- Who do you confide in?

6. Checking understanding and close

a. Did you specifically ask if the colleague understood?
Did you ask? If not, why not? Remember it is not enough to assume they know what is happening. You need to *show* the assessor that you have asked.

b. Is there a follow up or next meeting planned?
Whatever happened in your scenario, follow-up is important in this case. Alex needs on going support. As an F2 in General Practice you will only be there a short time. Did you think about finding someone else in the practice to support Alex?

c. Did you finish in 10 minutes?

Role Play 3.4 | Discussion

1. **Create a safe environment and read the doctor's brief given to you**

   a. **Read, read and read again!**
   The first thing to do is read the brief. Read it and read it again. Did you do that? Did you get halfway through the scenario and forget something and have to refer back to the brief?

   Next ask yourself: "What do I know from the brief?"

   In this case, you know you are to meet the health visitor and you have been told it is about a child with whom you have had no contact. She has been seen at the practice routinely with no problems documented.

   Start to think about why he/she could want to see you. Don't make assumptions, but start to pinpoint areas from the *Simplified assessment criteria for role play* on page 35 that could be relevant in this case. If you start to think of these before they come in, then you are more likely to ask appropriate questions.

   Remember this is your colleague!

   b. **Move the furniture if you need to and put your watch where you can see it**
   Did you move the furniture?
   Were you sitting too close or too far away from them?
   Was it comfortable?

2. **Introduction and active listening**

   a. **Start the conversation sensibly**
   You did not have the health visitors name in this brief. It is always better to use names. Did you ask? If not, why not?

   - Hi, Sorry I didn't get your name from the message I received...
   - Hello, I'm doctor... I understand you are the health visitor. Can I ask your name?

225

You may want to start the scenario with an open question.

- Hi, you asked to talk to me.........
- How can I help?

By asking this kind of open questions, you will allow them to talk, which will allow you to find out exactly why they have come to see you.

Niki wants support. She wants someone other than her to assess the mother and chid. Did you pick up on that or did you refer to social services?

Do not add any information to the brief unless they tell you that information. Just as in real life, the only things we know are written down or told to us during a meeting. We don't make things up in real life. Don't do it in the role play.

b. What is the colleague's expectation?

Did you ask what they wanted?

- How do you think I can help you today?
- What are you worried about?
- Is there anything else you would like to talk about?

Was there a hidden agenda? The hidden agenda was regarding a child who died under Niki's care previously. Did you find out?

c. Are you listening, looking and feeling the emotions?

Did you listen and give them time to talk?
Did you allow them to tell you why they were there?
If they were quiet, did you encourage them to talk using open questions?
Did you use any silence?
Did you look, listen and feel?
Did you listen to what they were saying?
Did you listen to what they were not saying?
Did you look and see how they behaved?
What was their body language saying?
Did you feel any emotions they gave out?
Did you feel any emotions evoked in you?

Were they sad, angry, nervous or agitated?

3. Verbal communication

a. Explanations of diagnoses and plans of action should be clear and pitched at the correct level

Explanations and discussions with a colleague are as important as with a patient. Did you remember that Niki was a health visitor? Detailed medical terminology is not appropriate in this case. Did you ensure you pitched to conversation at the right level?

With no evidence of neglect (the brief implied strongly that Deavon is well cared for) there is no reason at the moment to refer her to social services. Indeed Niki has tried this and social services have refused the case with no evidence of neglect or abuse.

It may be that once you see Deavon and her mother that you feel social services need to be involved too, but you need to arrange to see them to make that decision. This is also what Niki wants. She wants to SHARE the responsibility in this case. She is frightened about being the sole health care provider assessing this family.

Management could include the following:
i.   Calling the mother and talk to her.
ii.   Calling the child in for a "routine" check up.
iii. Calling mum and be honest, stating that there has been some concerns raised and that you would like to talk to her.
iv.   Going to a health visitor clinic that you know the mother will be attending to see them.
v.   Going on a home visit with the health visitor.

b. Clinical questioning (if appropriate) should show safe practice

Asking Niki about the health and welfare of Deavon is important here. Is she growing? Is she well dressed? Is there any evidence of bruising? How does mum interact with her at the clinic?

You know from your own records that mum has brought Deavon for her immunisations and baby checks.

c. Have you given the colleague choice?

Did you ask Niki if they had any ideas about what they wanted?

227

- How can I help you with this?
- In what way would you like me to be involved?

4. Non verbal communication

a. Your body language (did you remain calm?)
How was your eye contact?
Are you a floor or ceiling thinker?
Do you think you were too close/too far away from Niki?
Did you notice any irritating habits?

b. Did you pick up on the colleague's body language?
Were there any hairy moments?
Did the colleague get upset?
How did you respond to this?
Did you feel yourself becoming emotionally involved, angry or irritated?
What did you do to resolve it?
What would you do next time?

c. Was there a hidden agenda?
Hopefully you realised that Niki just wanted support. She wanted you to see the child and make an assessment. Did you offer?

5. Relevant psychosocial information
The psychosocial section is still important with colleagues.

Psychological
- How are you?
- Are you worried about anything?
- Is there anything in your mind?
- How are you coping with this?
- Is there anything else worrying you?

Financial
Not appropriate in this case

Social
- Is there anyone at home?
- Do you have anyone to talk to about this?

Spiritual
- Who do you confide in?

6. Checking understanding and close

a. Did you specifically ask if the colleague understood?
Did you ask? If not, why not? Remember it is not enough to assume they know what is happening. You need to *show* the assessor that you have asked.

b. Is there a follow up or next meeting planned?
Whatever happened in your scenario, follow-up is important in this case. Deavon needs to be seen by someone other than Niki and Niki needs feedback on that meeting if she is not due to be present. Remember when a colleague asks for help, it is our duty – working in a multidisciplinary team – to show support.

c. Did you finish in 10 minutes?

Role Play 3.5   Discussion

1. **Create a safe environment and read the doctor's brief given to you**

   a. **Read, read and read again!**
   The first thing to do is read the brief. Read it and read it again. Did you do that? Did you get halfway through the scenario and forget something and have to refer back to the brief?

   Next ask yourself: "What do I know from the brief?"

   In this case you have very little information other than a receptionist wants to talk to you.

   Start to think about why he/she could want to see you. Don't make assumptions, but start to pinpoint areas from the *Simplified assessment criteria for role play* on page 35 that could be relevant in this case. If you start to think of these before they come in, then you are more likely to ask appropriate questions.

   Remember this is your colleague!

   b. **Move the furniture if you need to and put your watch where you can see it**
   Did you move the furniture?
   Were you sitting too close or too far away from them?
   Was it comfortable?

2. **Introduction and active listening**

   a. **Start the conversation sensibly**
   Did you use the receptionist's name? If not, why not? It was in the brief.

   You may want to start the scenario with an open question.

   - Hi Stevie, are you ok?
   - How can I help?
   - You wanted to chat to me.........

By asking this kind of open questions, you will allow them to talk, which will allow you to find out exactly why they have come to see you.

Stevie is frightened and wants to go home. There is a hidden agenda here too. Did you find it? Look at the actor's brief and you will see that the receptionist wants to leave this job and find another one. Did you work it out?

Do not add any information to the brief unless they tell you that information. Just as in real life, the only things we know are written down or told to us during a meeting. We don't make things up in real life. Don't do it in the role play.

b. What is the colleague's expectation?
Did you ask what they wanted?

- How do you think I can help you today?
- What are you worried about?
- Is there anything else you would like to talk about?
- What do you want me to do?

There is a huge hidden agenda that may have remained hidden in this case. Stevie wants to leave the practice and is unhappy. If you missed this try rerunning the role play concentrating on the psychosocial history.

c. Are you listening, looking and feeling the emotions?
Did you listen and give them time to talk?
Did you allow them to tell you why they were there?
If they were quiet, did you encourage them to talk using open questions?
Did you use any silence?
Did you look, listen and feel?
Did you listen to what they were saying?
Did you listen to what they were not saying?
Did you look and see how they behaved?
What was their body language saying?
Did you feel any emotions they gave out?
Did you feel any emotions evoked in you?
Were they sad, angry, nervous or agitated?

3. Verbal communication

a. Explanations of diagnoses and plans of action should be clear and pitched at the correct level

Stevie is a receptionist and so you should not use medical jargon. Did you aim the explanation at the right level?

The plan of action could involve (amongst other things) the following:

i. Listening and offering support
ii. Referring the problem to a senior partner by offering to telephone them or talk to them at a later date face to face
iii. Referring the problem to the practice manager who is the receptionists line manager
iv. Offering to let the receptionist sit away from the main desk until a more senior person arrives
v. Agreeing that the receptionist can go home (although this is not strictly your responsibility) in order to make her feel safe and agree to tell the practice manger or senior partner when they return. If you do this, you must also ensure that reception is covered by someone else.
vi. Offering to contact the aggressive patient with a view to seeing them to assess if they need any further help.

You must not agree to strike the patient off the list!

b. Clinical questioning (if appropriate) should show safe practice

You could try and ask more information about the patient from the receptionist, but they will not know. You will need to look in the patient notes. You could – during your role play state

- Stevie, I need to have a look in the patient notes to find out a bit more about them. Do you know their name?"

This way you are SHOWING the assessor that you are thinking.

In addition, the disruption should be documented in the patient notes, to ensure every person in the practice knows that the patient can be aggressive. You could say:

> - I'm going to have a look in the notes to find out more about the patient and also make a brief entry about them coming into the practice today

This way the examiner KNOWS what you want to do.

c. Have you given the colleague choice?
Did you ask Stevie how they wanted you to help?
How can I help you with this?
In what way would you like me to be involved?
What can I do to make this better for you?

4. Non verbal communication

a. Your body language (did you remain calm?)
How was your eye contact?
Are you a floor or ceiling thinker?
Do you think you were too close/too far away from Stevie?
Did you notice any irritating habits?

b. Did you pick up on the colleague's body language?
Were there any hairy moments?
Did the receptionist get upset?
How did you respond to this?
Did you feel yourself becoming emotionally involved, angry or irritated?
What did you do to resolve it?
What would you do next time?

c. Was there a hidden agenda?
There was a hidden agenda but it may have been difficult to elicit. Don't worry if you didn't find out that Stevie was unhappy at work and wanted to leave; just remember with every role play you must ask some psychosocial questions.

5. Relevant psychosocial information
The psychosocial section is still important with colleagues.

Psychological
- How are you?
- You look worried. Is it just this or is there something else?

- Is there anything else you want to talk about?

Financial
If you found out that Stevie wanted to go on sick leave, you could ask:
- "How will you manage financially if you're on leave?"

Social
- Is there anyone at home
- Do you have anyone to talk to about this?
- How will you get home?
- Do you have anyone who can come and pick you up?

Spiritual
- Who do you confide in?

6. **Checking understanding and close**

a. **Did you specifically ask if the colleague understood?**
Did you ask? If not, why not? Remember it is not enough to assume they know what is happening. You need to *show* the assessor that you have asked.

b. **Is there a follow up or next meeting planned?**
Whatever happened in your scenario, follow-up is important in this case. Stevie is a valued member of staff who has been upset by a patient. Whether she leaves the practice or not, the practice manager and one of the partners need to know what happened to her and how she responded. You must also ensure that feedback is given to Stevie.

- Would you like me to call you later to make sure you are ok?
- Shall I call you and let you know what the practice manager says?
- Next time you're in work, come and chat to me so I can make sure you're ok.

c. **Did you finish in 10 minutes?**

Role Play 3.6 Discussion

1. **Create a safe environment and read the doctor's brief given to you**

   a. **Read, read and read again!**

   b. **Move the furniture if you need to and put your watch where you can see it**

2. **(***) Introduction and active listening**

   a. **Start the conversation sensibly**

   b. **What is the colleague's expectation?**
   Did you realise that Lee wanted to off load the responsibility of this problem?

   c. **Are you listening, looking and feeling the emotions?**

3. **(***) Verbal communication**

   a. **Explanations of diagnoses and plans of action should be clear and pitched at the correct level**
   Lee is a midwife and so you can use some medical terminology with them. Did you pitch your discussion at the correct level?

   Your plan of action should include:

   i. Taking all of the information from Lee and ensuring you have accurate documentation of the discussion

   ii. Ensure that Lee knows you are taking her concerns seriously

   iii. You can then either offer to approach the senior partner yourself, explain that you need to involve a more senior colleague or advise Lee that you need to call the practice manager.

Whenever there is a concern raised over a colleague's performance, your first duty is to the patient. You must ensure your patients are safe immediately. In this case, because the potential danger is with a very senior colleague, you may not feel able to confront the partner. You must assess the danger to the patient wither yourself, or immediately report this to a senior colleague – the practice manager or to another partner.

If you feel able to confront the partner, you could go to see them to check whether you too can smell alcohol and then discuss the midwife's concerns. It is important to document the conversations that you have in case you need to refer to them in the future.

    b. Clinical questioning (if appropriate) should show safe practice

    c. Have you given the colleague choice?

4. Non verbal communication

    a. Your body language (did you remain calm?)

    b. Did you pick up on the colleague's body language?

    c. Was there a hidden agenda?
    Did you realise that Lee just wanted to hand over the responsibility?

5. Psychosocial influences
Psychological, social, financial, spiritual

6. Checking understanding and close

    a. Did you specifically ask if the colleague understood?

    b. Is there a follow up or next meeting planned?

    c. Did you finish in 10 minutes?

Role Play 3.7 | Discussion

1. (***) **Create a safe environment and read the doctor's brief given to you**

    a. **Read, read and read again!**
        Did you start to plan what you were going to say before the student came in? Did you look at the form carefully? Did you remember that you needed to fill the form in?

    b. **Move the furniture if you need to and put your watch where you can see it**

2. **Introduction and active listening**

    a. **Start the conversation sensibly**

    b. **What is the colleague's expectation?**

    c. **Are you listening, looking and feeling the emotions?**

3. (***) **Verbal communication**

    a. **Explanations of diagnoses and plans of action should be clear and pitched at the correct level**
        This is a medical student. Did you use appropriate language? Did you explain that you had to submit the form to the deanery?

    b. **Clinical questioning (if appropriate) should show safe practice**

    c. **Have you given the colleague choice?**
        Did you ask what the medical student thought you should put on the form? With difficult assessments, it sometimes helps to ask the student to grade themselves before you do. Most of the time people over-grade themselves. At least it is a starting point from which you can explain how you are going to grade them. In this case, you must put 'poor'. You have not seen this student and therefore cannot comment that they are average or higher. If the

237

student tells you about their home situation, you can add a comment (if they agree) explaining mitigating circumstances. It would be inappropriate to grade the student as good or excellent just because they ask.

4. **Non verbal communication**

   a. **Your body language (did you remain calm?)**

   b. **Did you pick up on the colleague's body language?**

   c. **Was there a hidden agenda?**

5. **(***) Psychosocial influences**
   Psychological, social, financial, spiritual

   Remember it is important even with colleagues to ask.
   Did you find out about their daughter? Did you ask about their financial situation? Did you discover they were self funding?

6. **Checking understanding and close**

   a. **Did you specifically ask if the colleague understood?**

   b. **Is there a follow up or next meeting planned?**

   c. **Did you finish in 10 minutes?**

Role Play 3.8 | Discussion

1. (***) **Create a safe environment and read the doctor's brief given to you**

    a. **Read, read and read again!**
        The person coming to see you is a pharmacist. In the brief you have only prescribed 2 drugs, the penicillin and the diclofenac. Did you start to think about these drugs before the actor came in?

    b. **Move the furniture if you need to and put your watch where you can see it**

2. (***) **Introduction and active listening**

    a. **Start the conversation sensibly**

    b. **What is the colleague's expectation?**

    c. **Are you listening, looking and feeling the emotions?**
        Did you feel how angry the pharmacist was? Angry colleagues and patients can be very daunting. Before engaging with them you first need to try to calm them down. Having someone shouting at you whilst standing up is often very difficult.

        Try the following:

        i.   Get them to sit down.

        ii. Use their name.

        iii. Speak calmly and do not raise your voice to their level

        iv. If they refuse to sit down, do not remain standing. Sit down yourself and again ask if they will sit with you. Often this is enough to dissipate some of their anger. Obviously, if they remain standing and shouting and you feel intimidated then you may need to stand up again. Try perching on the edge of the table so you are sitting but closer to their eye level.

239

v. Repeat the same phrase over and over until they either sit or show signs of calming. For example:

- Mr/Mrs X. Can you please sit down and talk to me……..
- Mr/Mrs X. I would really rather you sat with me so we can talk about this properly……

vi. Reflecting their anger back, showing empathy. For example:

- Mr/Mrs X. I can see you are really angry about this…..
- I am sorry you feel so angry about this…….

vi. Try apologising, this is often what people want and can sometimes dissipate their anger altogether. For example:

- Mr/Mrs Sunar, I am so sorry about the penicillin. Can I have a look at the casualty card to refresh my memory?

Note: Always remember that your own safety is paramount. In the role play, no actor is going to attack you. In real life, unfortunately, this is not so. If you feel intimidated or threatened by a patient then either leave the room or call for help. Many GP practices have panic buttons. Most hospital beds have emergency cords. Do not ever put yourself in a situation in real life where you are at risk.

3. (***) Verbal communication

a. **Explanations of diagnoses and plans of action should be clear and pitched at the correct level**
Did you make a plan of action? Did you promise to be more careful in the future?

If the pharmacist threatened you with a review of your notes, did you ask to meet to see the results? Did you offer to review the notes yourself? Doing an audit of ones work can be a great teaching/ learning exercise.

b. **Clinical questioning (if appropriate) should show safe practice**
You could ask to see the casualty card to check the entry here.

c. **Have you given the colleague choice?**

4. **(***) Non verbal communication**

a. **Your body language (did you remain calm?)**
In view of how angry the pharmacist was, did you remain calm?
Was your voice relaxed? Was your eye contact non-threatening?
Did you sit?
When faced with an angry person, it is often wise to try to avoid threatening gestures such as pointing and large hand gestures.
Did you find yourself becoming more and more uptight the longer the pharmacist was shouting?

Try the scenario again paying close attention to your own body language. You really need to get the pharmacist to sit down. It is much more difficult to be angry if you are sitting!

b. **Did you pick up on the colleague's body language?**
Did you realise they were angry when they came in?
Did you notice how their anger subsided when they sat?

c. **Was there a hidden agenda?**

5. **(***) Psychosocial influences**
Psychological, social, financial, spiritual

Remember with colleagues this is still important!

Did you find out about Mr/Mrs Sunar's bad start to the day? Did you find out about their resentment of the change over of doctors? If not, why not?

Get the pharmacist to sit down and ensure you psychosocial questions:

- Are you ok?

- Is there anything else bothering you? You seem to be really angry.
- How are things with you?

6. **Checking understanding and close**

   a. **Did you specifically ask if the colleague understood?**

   b. **Is there a follow up or next meeting planned?**

   c. **Did you finish in 10 minutes?**

Role Play 3.9 | Discussion

1. **Create a safe environment and read the doctor's brief given to you**

   a. **Read, read and read again!**

   b. **Move the furniture if you need to and put your watch where you can see it**

2. **(***) Introduction and active listening**

   a. **Start the conversation sensibly**

   b. **What is the colleague's expectation?**
   This is simply a fact-finding role play. The aim for the assessor is to find out more about you and your personality. How you coped and how you feel about medicine. Be honest.

   c. **Are you listening, looking and feeling the emotions?**

3. **(***) Verbal communication**

   a. **Explanations of diagnoses and plans of action should be clear and pitched at the correct level**
   This is an experienced and intelligent nurse, did you pitch the conversation at the right level?

   Did they ask you about how the medical students would feel having a nurse with them? This is a way for the assessors to find out what you really think about nurses. Did you show that you respected your colleagues?

   b. **Clinical questioning (if appropriate) should show safe practice**

   c. **Have you given the colleague choice?**

243

4. **Non verbal communication**

    a. **Your body language**

    b. **Did you pick up on the colleague's body language?**

    c. **Was there a hidden agenda?**

5. **Psychosocial influences**
   Psychological, social, financial, spiritual

6. **Checking understanding and close**

    a. **Did you specifically ask if the colleague understood?**

    b. **Is there a follow up or next meeting planned?**

    c. **Did you finish in 10 minutes?**

Role Play 3.10 | Discussion

1. **Create a safe environment and read the doctor's brief given to you**

   a. **Read, read and read again!**

   b. **Move the furniture if you need to and put your watch where you can see it**

2. **(***) Introduction and active listening**

   a. **Start the conversation sensibly**

   b. **What is the colleague's expectation?**

   c. **Are you listening, looking and feeling the emotions?**
   Did you realise how frightened they were?
   Did you feel their agitation?

3. **(***) Verbal communication**

   a. **Explanations of diagnoses and plans of action should be clear and pitched at the correct level**
   The plan of action is very important here.

      i. **Calm the nurse down** to have a detailed conversation.

      ii. **Make the patient safe.** Contact the pharmacy helpline (the nurse knows about this, did you find out?) to see if the patient is at risk then contact the patient to review them and explain what has happened.

      iii. **Initiate an incident report or a significant event analysis.** This is not done to apportion blame but to systematically analyse the sequence of events that lead to the "mistake" happening. The aim is to identify events that could be improved to prevent it happening again. This may include retraining or supervision of the nurse in this case.

    iv. **Involve a senior member of staff** - the practice manager or a senior partner.

b. **Clinical questioning (if appropriate) should show safe practice**
The patient needs to be seen and reviewed.

c. **Have you given the colleague choice?**

4. **(***) Non verbal communication**

a. **Your body language (did you remain calm?)**

b. **Did you pick up on the colleague's body language?**
Did you realise the nurse was anxious and overloaded with work?

c. **Was there a hidden agenda?**

5. **Psychosocial influences**
Psychological, social, financial, spiritual

6. **Checking understanding and close**

a. **Did you specifically ask if the colleague understood?**

b. **Is there a follow up or next meeting planned?**

c. **Did you finish in 10 minutes?**

Role Play 3.11 | Discussion

1. **(***) Create a safe environment and read the doctor's brief given to you**

   a. **Read, read and read again!**
   This is slightly more complex as there is information in the brief that you need. Did you read it carefully? Did you make notes?

   b. **Move the furniture if you need to and put your watch where you can see it**

2. **Introduction and active listening**

   a. **Start the conversation sensibly**

   b. **What is the colleague's expectation?**

   c. **Are you listening, looking and feeling the emotions?**

3. **(***) Verbal communication**

   a. **Explanations of diagnoses and plans of action should be clear and pitched at the correct level**
   Charlie is very unhelpful. You need to offer solutions to your own problem. Did you apologise to Charlie for the inconvenience? Did you get him/her on side? If you are polite and kind to someone showing them respect, it is more likely that they will help you. Did this work?

   You could offer the following:

   i. **Ask for a locum to cover**

   ii. **Offer to take unpaid leave**

   iii. **Offer to try to find another doctor in the hospital** (not currently doing medicine) to cover for "locum rates"

247

iv.   Offer to pay for a locum

Try not to resort to threats such as:

- "Well I'll just call in sick then"
- "I'm going to the wedding anyway. I'm giving you 2 weeks notice, it's up to you whether you cover it or not.""

When we are desperate, we are often angry at the confines of our medical rotas. It doesn't seem fair that other professions have every weekend off. Unfortunately, this is part of the career that you chose. There must be a way to go to the wedding, you just need to find a solution.

The ideal compromise – if the day doctor agrees to it – is for the person working on the Saturday daytime to extend their shift and work later – for example until midnight. Look back to the brief, it states that the wedding is LOCAL. You could then attend the wedding all day Saturday and into the evening and then go to work. You would then be able to sleep all day Sunday to recover before going to work Sunday night and repay the day doctor at a later date.

You would be sacrificing drinking alcohol at the wedding (if you drink) as you could not work after drinking and would need to leave early, but you could then attend most of the wedding.

Remember the role play is not real life. This is a way of finding out how you deal with non-medical colleagues and the respect that you show them. It also shows your thought processes when trying to problem solve and your negotiation skills.

b.   Clinical questioning (if appropriate) should show safe practice

c.   Have you given the colleague choice?

4. **(***) Non verbal communication**

   a. **Your body language (did you remain calm?)**
      When we don't get a positive reaction to something that we want, even if we remain calm in our voices, our body language often gives us away. Did you become frustrated? Did it show through your body?

   b. **Did you pick up on the colleague's body language?**

   c. **Was there a hidden agenda?**

5. **Psychosocial influences**
   Psychological, social, financial, spiritual

6. **Checking understanding and close**

   a. **Did you specifically ask if the colleague understood?**

   b. **Is there a follow up or next meeting planned?**

   c. **Did you finish in 10 minutes?**

Role Play 3.12 Discussion

1. **Create a safe environment and read the doctor's brief given to you**

   a. **Read, read and read again!**

   b. **Move the furniture if you need to and put your watch where you can see it**

2. **(***) Introduction and active listening**

   a. **Start the conversation sensibly**

   b. **What is the colleague's expectation?**
   Did you agree to the confidential chat? Did you realise that Hans was not going to open up to you unless you agreed? What did you then do when you realised how serious this allegation was? Did you still maintain confidentiality?

   c. **Are you listening, looking and feeling the emotions?**

3. **(***) Verbal communication**

   a. **Explanations of diagnoses and plans of action should be clear and pitched at the correct level**
   In this case it is currently speculation that Frechna is taking the Pethidine for herself. We only have the word of a midwife who has looked "briefly" at a couple of patient notes.

      i. The first thing to ensure is that the patients are safe. Did you find out that Frechna is currently away from work and not due to return until tomorrow? It was in the actor's brief, but they were instructed not to tell you unless you asked where she was.

      Since she is away from work the patients are safe. Frechna may not be, but your first responsibility is to the patients.

ii.   Next an investigation needs to happen to find out whether the drugs really are missing. This really needs involvement of the labour ward manager or a senior member of staff. Did you insist on telling someone?

You could agree to an informal investigation where you and Hans take a look to see if Hans' suspicion is correct. If you then find out that he/she is telling the truth you MUST report this. Missing controlled drugs is a serious offence. Frechna should be officially investigated by the labour ward manager, firstly to see if the problem exists and if there is evidence pointing to Frechna, how serious the problem is.

This must not be covered up, no matter what the personal circumstances are.

iii.   An incident report needs to be filed or an official complaint made verbally to the labour ward manager. You cannot take this case on yourself as an F2 doctor. It is likely that Frechna will be questioned on return to work the following day; she may be suspended while an investigation takes place.

One of the points in the GMC's "Good medical practice" (see www.gmc-uk.org) is that it is your responsibility to protect patients from your colleague's conduct, performance or ill health. Don't forget to read this document before your assessment!

b. Clinical questioning (if appropriate) should show safe practice
You need to ensure the patients are safe. Did you?

c. Have you given the colleague choice?
In this case the midwife needs reporting, so although you can give your colleague options, the ultimate outcome should be the involvement of a senior member of staff.

- Frechna needs reporting to the senior midwife/ labour ward manager. Either you can do this or I will. What would you prefer?
- I'm sorry; we can't delay reporting this it is too important. Would you like to write the incident report or shall I?

4. **(***) Non verbal communication**

   a. **Your body language (did you remain calm?)**
   Did you remain calm when you realised you had to break the confidence of your colleague?

   b. **Did you pick up on the colleague's body language?**

   c. **Was there a hidden agenda?**

5. **(***) Psychosocial influences**
   Psychological, social, financial, spiritual

   Did you find out about all the problems Frechna was having? If not, read the actor's brief and run the role play again. Don't forget this section.

6. **(***) Checking understanding and close**

   a. **Did you specifically ask if the colleague understood?**

   b. **Is there a follow up or next meeting planned?**
   Who are you reporting this to and when?

   c. **Did you finish in 10 minutes?**

Role Play 3.13 | Discussion

1. **Create a safe environment and read the doctor's brief given to you**

   a. **Read, read and read again!**

   b. **Move the furniture if you need to and put your watch where you can see it**

2. **(***) Introduction and active listening**

   a. **Start the conversation sensibly**
      There was no information about the nurse other than they were from the ward. Did you ask for their name? Did you ask what level they were, or which ward they were from? Unless the name is in the brief, you need to ask for it!

   b. **What is the colleague's expectation?**
      Did you give in and prescribe?

   c. **Are you listening, looking and feeling the emotions?**

3. **(***) Verbal communication**

   a. **Explanations of diagnoses and plans of action should be clear and pitched at the correct level**
      All hospitals have their own guidelines for prescribing for staff. The general rule of thumb is that you should not prescribe for anyone who is not a true patient of yours. This means you should avoid (if possible) prescribing for family, friends and colleagues.

      The way to make the nurse your "patient" is to register them with A&E and then see, assess and prescribe for them if appropriate. The nurse will have told you they did not have time for that. There are ways of making that process faster:

    i.   The nurse could register and then go back to the ward. When their turn came up, you could call them to come back down for 10 minutes to see them.

    ii.   You could get the nurse to give their details to reception and then see them immediately. This is not fair to the other patients waiting in A&E to be seen but since it is for the greater good of other patients on the ward you could suggest this.

    iii.   You could assess the nurse there and then and decide if they needed antibiotics choosing the type they require. Then suggest they quickly go and register and go back to the ward. If the receptionists passed the casualty card on to you once it was completed you could then fill it in with the details, arrange the antibiotics and have them sent to the ward.

b. Clinical questioning (if appropriate) should show safe practice
Did you ask to examine them? Did you ask about allergies?

c. Have you given the colleague choice?

4. Non verbal communication

    a. Your body language (did you remain calm?)

    b. Did you pick up on the colleague's body language?

    c. Was there a hidden agenda?

5. Psychosocial influences
Psychological, social, financial, spiritual

6. Checking understanding and close

    a. Did you specifically ask if the colleague understood?

    b. Is there a follow up or next meeting planned?

    c. Did you finish in 10 minutes?

Role Play 3.14 Discussion

1. **(***) Create a safe environment and read the doctor's brief given to you**

    a. **Read, read and read again!**
        You have a significant amount of clinical information here about the patient you are going to discuss. Did you remember it? Did you need to refer to the notes?

        Did you suspect what the discussion was going to be about before the occupational therapist came in?

    b. **Move the furniture if you need to and put your watch where you can see it**

2. **(***) Introduction and active listening**

    a. **Start the conversation sensibly**

    b. **What is the colleaue's expectation?**
        Did you agree to override the consultant's decision and keep the patient in hospital? Remember your duty is to the patient first and to ensure their safety. As a minimum you should have offered to try to contact the consultant. Look back at your brief. It states that your consultant is unavailable. If you do not feel able to make the decision yourself, then there are always other consultants or senior doctors within the hospital that you can refer to.

    c. **Are you listening, looking and feeling the emotions?**

3. **(***) Verbal communication**

    a. **Explanations of diagnoses and plans of action should be clear and pitched at the correct level**
        Remember the patient's safety comes first. If they are not safe for discharge then something needs to be done to protect them

Your plan of action could include:

i.   Delay the ambulance for 6 hours until the consultant returns

ii.   Offer to talk to the patient to see if she is willing to stay voluntarily

iii.   Suggest admitting Mrs Day into an NHS bed if she cannot afford the private one.

iv.   Ask the occupational therapist if she could do the home visit today. You could ask the ambulance service if you could use the discharge ambulance booked to take the patient home and then return later following her home assessment. By this time the consultant would be back in the hospital.

    b. Clinical questioning (if appropriate) should show safe practice

    c. Have you given the colleague choice?

4. Non verbal communication

    a. Your body language (did you remain calm?)

    b. Did you pick up on the colleague's body language?

    c. Was there a hidden agenda?

5. (***) Psychosocial influences
Psychological, social, financial, spiritual
Did you work out that the occupational therapist was feeling undermined by medical staff?

6. Checking understanding and close

    a. Did you specifically ask if the colleague understood?

    b. Is there a follow up or next meeting planned?

    c. Did you finish in 10 minutes?

Role Play 3.15 Discussion

1. (***) **Create a safe environment and read the doctor's brief given to you**

   a. **Read, read and read again!**
   Did you remember that you thought the receptionist was good at their job and always polite? Check the brief again.

   b. **Move the furniture if you need to and put your watch where you can see it**

2. (***) **Introduction and active listening**

   a. **Start the conversation sensibly**

   b. **What is the colleague's expectation?**

   c. **Are you listening, looking and feeling the emotions?**
   Did you "feel" the receptionists worry? Did you pick up on their tiredness? If you did, how soon into the scenario? Did you comment on it the minute you noticed Phil was tired?

   - You look tired... are you ok?

3. (***) **Verbal communication**

   a. **Explanations of diagnoses and plans of action should be clear and pitched at the correct level**
   This colleague needs your support. Your plan of action is mainly to listen and support. You could suggest she/he takes some compassionate leave. You could offer to talk to the practice manager. You could offer to write a character reference for them to help with the complaint.

   b. **Clinical questioning (if appropriate) should show safe practice**

   c. **Have you given the colleague choice?**

257

4. (***) **Non verbal communication**

    a. **Your body language (did you remain calm?)**

    b. **Did you pick up on the colleague's body language?**
        Did you pick up on the colleague's tiredness through their body language early? Did the colleague need to verbalise their tiredness with a yawn before you noticed?

        Remember when you notice something. Verbalise it.

        - "You look tired, are you ok?"
        - "Are you sleeping ok, you look tired"

    c. **Was there a hidden agenda?**

5. (***) **Psychosocial influences**
    Psychological, social, financial, spiritual

    Did you find out about their father? Did you realise that they were visiting every day and were exhausted?

6. **Checking understanding and close**

    a. **Did you specifically ask if the colleague understood?**

    b. **Is there a follow up or next meeting planned?**

    c. **Did you finish in 10 minutes?**

K Task prioritisation
Introduction & techniques

The second exercise that you will be assessed upon in your selection centre is the prioritisation exercise. It is a written paper.

This exercise is very different from the role play task. It is individually tested and is purely based on what you write down. There is no personal interaction and it is marked in your absence after you have completed the task.

The key to success with this exercise is to practise on as many examples as you can within the allocated time limit set by the selection centre. With an unlimited amount of time, this task would be much easier; faced with only 30 minutes to complete this exercise adds a huge amount of time pressure, which makes the task much more difficult.

The prioritisation exercise is definitely testing your ability to solve problems and work under pressure of time, your professional probity, thought processes and personal organisation. As you will see later it is also possibly testing your multidisciplinary team working skills and the effect upon you. The most important piece of advice I can give you is to remember to talk about the *effect upon you*. This is a key aspect of the prioritisation exercise and is often forgotten.

Well-run courses specifically aimed at the GPST interview process will go through examples of the prioritisation exercise in detail. They will also ideally allow you to practise in an examination style environment with the pressure of time added. If you cannot attend a course, at least practise the examples that follow in the book. Be tough on yourself. Perhaps try the first one or a few with no time limit, but make sure that you save at least one to do while the clock is ticking. It adds a completely different perspective to the task.

What will happen?

Read the information sent to you from your selection centre. Typically you are given 30 minutes to complete the prioritisation task. This is usually split into three sections:

- Ranking
- Explaining the ranking
- Reflecting

You will be taken as a group to an examination-type room and sat at individual desks with an invigilator present. This person is not assessing you during the exercise. Experienced examiners will score your paper after completion of the task once you have handed in your paper and left the room. All candidates in your group will start the exercise at the same time.

The exercise

The exercise is the same in all centres. You will be given a group of simultaneous tasks that you need to rank in order of importance to perform. These tasks are usually based in primary or secondary care and you must answer them from your own perspective. The paper will tell you either:

a. ***You are a doctor in secondary care***
   In this case you are likely to be an A&E or ward doctor (F2 level) and have a number of sequential bleeps with tasks to complete. These tasks will be listed.

b. ***You are a doctor based in primary care***
   In this case you are likely to be an F2 doctor based in General Practice and have a list of tasks to complete. This is either in the form of messages left for you or sequential telephone calls. These tasks will be listed.

Not only are you asked to rank the tasks in the order that you would perform them but you also need to justify the order by explaining HOW you would complete each task and WHY you would put each task in the order that you did.

The question paper

The question and answer paper is usually set in two main ways:

Type 1 – In order of receipt (Least common)

The paper will have an introductory statement about who you are and where you are based. It will then list each of the tasks in the order that they were received, in the form of a series of stems followed by a blank box below each stem where you can write your justification. This box limits your space for explanation to only four or five lines of writing.

For each stem, there will be a small box for you to place the ranking order into.

There are two ways to approach this type of paper:

a. Go through and justify each stem and then, at the end, ensure that you have saved some time (which is often in limited supply) to rank the tasks in the order that you would do them.

b. First spend a few minutes deciding on the order that you would complete each task and rank them. Follow this by placing the justification in the boxes provided.

There is no right or wrong way to approach this paper. It very much depends on the manner with which you analyse situations. By practising these exercises with a time limit, you will begin to work out which approach works better for you.

You need to work out your own approach. Do not regurgitate what is written here. Instead, use this book as a platform to provide you with ideas to try out to enable you to create your own style and approach.

Figure 6. Type 1 prioritisation paper

Stem explaining that you are a doctor in primary or secondary care who has received a group of sequential messages or bleeps.

Text of Message 1

Ranking number ☐

Text of Message 2

Ranking number ☐

Text of Message 3

Ranking number ☐

Text of Message 4

Ranking number ☐

(In practice, there will likely be five or six messages to order and justify.)

Type 2 – In order of priority (Most common)

The principles are exactly the same as with the type 1 paper but you have to write the justifications in the order that you would perform the tasks.

The paper will have an introductory statement about who you are and where you are based and will list each of the tasks in the order that they were received. These will be numbered. You will then have a separate sheet with empty boxes. In the first box you will be expected to justify the first task that you would perform, in the second box the second, until the final task that you would leave to the very end.

The reason that this is more difficult is that you need to decide on the order of the tasks before you start to write. This often means making some very rapid decisions in the first few minutes of the assessment. Some of you will be very confident in doing this. For others who like to think and deliberate, it will take longer to make the decision. You may also feel less confident with the decisions made.

There are two ways to approach this type of paper:

a. First spend a few minutes deciding on the order that you would complete each task and then fill in the answer sheet in order from the first and most important task to the last and least important task.

b. Choose the task that you would obviously do first and fill in the first box. Choose the task that you would obviously do last and fill in the last box. Following this spend a few minutes thinking about the order of the rest and fill the boxes in as you see appropriate.

There is no right or wrong way to approach this paper. It will depend on your personality and confidence levels and the way that you analyse situations. By practising these exercises with a time limit, you will begin to work out which approach works better for you.

You need to work out your own approach. Do not regurgitate what is written here. Instead, use this book as a platform to provide you with ideas to try out to enable you to create your own style and approach.

Figure 7. Type 2 prioritisation paper

Stem explaining that you are a doctor in primary or secondary care who has received a group of sequential messages or bleeps.

Message 1
Message 2
Message 3
Message 4
etc.

Justify the tasks in the boxes below in the order that you would complete them. A is the first task that you would complete.

A – Message:

B – Message:

C – Message:

D – Message:

(There will likely be five or six messages to justify and rank)

Ranking

Make sure that you follow the instructions given to you on the day. If the paper asks you to rank using the letters A-F, use these letters and nothing else. If the paper asks you to number the ranking from 1 to 6, use these numbers.

This may seem obvious, but with the added pressure of time it is easy to forget to read the instruction carefully. As this exercise is testing how you cope under pressure, a simple mistake like this may lose you valuable points. Don't risk it!

The blank boxes

The defined blank boxes are there for a reason. If the instructions state that you should only write within the defined space, please adhere to that. The examiners are unlikely to read anything outside of the box if this instruction is given. Don't waste time writing information that will not be assessed. Time is precious.

Conversely, the boxes are there to be filled. The examiners will expect comprehensive explanations, so make sure that you provide comprehensive and well argued explanations. There is no need to fill the space for the sake of it, but usually you should expect to write a few lines of text in each box.

Mistakes

This task is assessing your thought processes under pressure. Try to make your decision about the order that you would complete the tasks before committing this decision to the paper.

By having a clear thought process you are likely to score more points. A paper with five different rankings that have been scribbled out and changed is unlikely to score highly.

If you are the type of person who is likely to change their mind, make notes elsewhere before committing to your decision. Use pencil that you can rub out. You may not allow scrap paper, as they want to see your thought processes written down.

Additional task – Reflective Learning

As well as ranking and justifying each task, you will be required to reflect on the exercise and the scenario given. This consists generally of about three questions of the type:

- What did you find challenging in this task?
- What you learnt from this exercise?
- What will you take away from it with regard to your future career?
- How will you implement your learnings in future?
- What did you think you did well?
- What would you do differently next time?
- What did you learn about yourself from this task?

Answering those questions is compulsory and must be done within the total 30-minute time period allocated to the scenario. You should therefore ensure that you allocate at least 5 minutes to complete that part of the exercise.

Those of you who have trained in the UK 'new system' will have often had experience of reflective learning through medical school and throughout your foundation years of training. It is important in all aspects of medicine, and General Practice has embraced it wholeheartedly. Those of you in the old "traditional" system of training or from overseas may have no experience at all and know little about it. Reflective learning is not a complex concept. It can in fact be applied to any exercise or task completed and is often done subconsciously by many people.

A common situation in medical practice where reflective learning is practised is following an arrest call. Imagine that you were part of an arrest team where the patient sadly died. Rather than returning to A&E to see the next patient on our list, we often spend a little time thinking about what happened, what went well, what could have been done differently, what we found difficult and how we felt about the arrest call. This is reflective thinking. If we use some of that thinking to alter and improve our practice next time, then we have learnt from our experience. This is reflective learning.

It often seems odd when you first start practising it but, like everything else we have discussed in this book, with practice it becomes easier and more natural.

Practise the reflective learning with each of the examples in the book. In addition, start practising every day to help this become a natural way of thinking. Set yourself a target to allocate 5 minutes each day to reflective learning. This can be done at work after seeing a patient; it could also be applied at home. An example of using it at home could be after making dinner. How well did it go? What did you do well? What did you find difficult? What would you do differently next time?

You can practise reflective learning at any time with any task. Remember, preparation and practise is the only way to improve.

Time

Time really is in short supply for this exercise. This factor alone increases the pressure attached to it. Try to plan your time as you practise the exercises in the book. You need to split the allocated time to ensure you complete the whole exercise.

In order to give effective answers, you must follow a thought process with which you are comfortable. Ultimately, you will each need to cover all of the following points, but it is up to you to decide what order to do them in.

1. **Read the brief**
   Who are you? Where are you? What criteria are given?
   Is it a type 1 or type 2 paper?
   Are you to use numbers or letters in your ranking?

   Read it, read it and read it again to make sure that you have understood the task.

2. **Think about the ranking**
   Is there an obvious task to do first and last? Obvious options would include anything that would prevent a risk to a patient.
   Is there a clear order for all of them?
   Are there one or two options that could be placed in any order? How are you going to decide where to rank them?

3. Decide on the ranking

You need to make a firm decision at some point in the exercise as to your final ranking order. Make this decision before confirming this on paper. Try not to make changes if you can.

4. Justify your answers

Each of the tasks needs to be justified. Explain how you would perform the task and why you would place it where you have.

5. Reflective learning

This part of the exercise is as important as the first part. There are points awarded for this section. Candidates in the past did not leave enough time to complete this section thoroughly as they thought that it was more important to finalise the justifications. Do not fall into this trap.

6. Check your answers

Ideally, as with any written task, a little time to check over your paper is always valuable. You may find that some of the rankings need tweaking or that you could justify one option more appropriately.

Effect on you

Some prioritisation tasks contain options that are of a more personal nature (i.e. they do not solely relate to patients). When facing such options, it is essential that you take into account how the situation is affecting you and your abilities to function both as a doctor and a human being.

Usually, at least one of the messages, tasks or bleeps listed will have a personal slant. This may be a personal phone call, a family crisis, an appointment that you need to keep or the fact that you are going on holiday. It is very important that you recognise their personal slant and that, in the justification, you write down how this would affect *you*.

There are several ways to approach this. I have met both extremes of doctors who would react very differently when faced with a personal message. As long as you justify clearly in your answer how it would affect you (if at all) then you can in theory place this in any order in the ranking.

For example:

You are an F2 in A&E and one of your six bleeps is a message left with the senior ward nurse who asks you to contact your sister urgently.

You could look at this and think:

a. **This is priority number 1** (depending on the rest of the messages), provided you justified it adequately.

My sister looks after my 1-year-old son whilst I am at work and the only time that she would ever call is if he were seriously ill.

You would need to back this up further by explaining the effect on you:

I would be unable to concentrate on any task in front of me, suspecting that my son was ill, and so I would have to call her immediately to find out what had happened. I would therefore place this task first in the ranking.

or

I would be unable to concentrate on any task in front of me suspecting that my son was ill. I would need more information as soon as was possible. I would ask the ward nurse to call my sister back and get a full message regarding what was wrong whilst I attended the next patient. I would ask the nurse to call another junior doctor to come and take over from me if it was a life or death situation in order for me to attend to my son.

Both justifications would allow you to rank your sister's call first.

b. **This is low priority**, as long as you justified it adequately.

My sister calls me at work every day at least once. She calls me at home about six times a day. Her urgent calls are always relating to a fashion question. Can she borrow my jumper? Can she wear red trousers with orange shoes? Knowing that this is what her question is likely to be, I would place it much lower down in the list of priorities. My patients always come first.

Depending on the other tasks, this type of justification would allow you to rank this "personal message" much lower down, perhaps even last.

The right answer

There is perhaps no absolute right and wrong way to order the messages or tasks; and much of the marking will be related to your justification. If you are aware of the GMC's *Good Medical Practice* (see www.gmc-uk.org), this task will be much easier. The GMC's *Duties of a Doctor* clearly states that your patient always comes first. You must remember this but, as mentioned above, do not forget the effect on you, as a person and as a doctor.

Approaches to ranking

One approach is to look at the messages/ tasks that need to be completed and split them into categories. Some tasks may have a direct relationship with patient safety (e.g. a patient with chest pain at your surgery); others are also patient-related but maybe not so urgent (e.g. a complaint). You then have a range of tasks which have no immediate effect on patients, (e.g. a colleague who wants to talk to you about an audit project). And finally, you have tasks which are of a personal nature (e.g. a phone call from your sister).

The tasks that will be presented to you will fit into one of these categories. There could be between one and three of each type in your list:

Figure 8: Suggested categorisation of tasks for prioritisation

Patient	**Clinical cases involving the patient directly**, e.g. chest pain, arrest call, nurse request to see a patient on the ward.
Extended patient	**Clinically associated cases involving non-urgent patient matters,** e.g. relatives, complaints, death.
Other	**No direct patient effect**, e.g. completing the rota, a telephone call, running late for a meeting.

In general, the prioritisation order should reflect the order of the above categories (i.e. direct patient related issues first, the extended patient issues next and then other issues). Remember, however, that tasks that have a personal slant may be ranked anywhere in the above scale depending on the effect that they may have on you. If a message or task is likely affect your ability to perform your job, justify it and place it higher up in the list of prioritisation.

Delegation

One of the most important questions to ask yourself before you start to write is: "Who have I got available to help?"

This task is not about you being a superhero doctor and coping with everything alone. In real practice, we have other people in the team to help. Think about who you can ask to help. This involves all members of the multidisciplinary team both clinical and non-clinical staff. Think about the whole team.

When delegating, it is essential that you ensure that the team member you entrusted with the task actually completed it. You can add a sentence to cover this in your answer.

Figure 9: Team support

▪ Junior doctor	▪ Social worker
▪ Senior doctor	▪ Health visitor
▪ Nurse	▪ Midwife
▪ Specialist nurse	▪ Patient and patient representatives
▪ Nurse Consultant	▪ Bereavement officer
▪ District/community nurse	▪ PALS
▪ Occupational therapist	▪ Support staff
▪ Physiotherapist	▪ Clerical staff
▪ Speech therapist	▪ Cleaners
▪ Pharmacist	

This is not an exhaustive list and you may be able to think of others.

Need for further information

In some cases, the options may be difficult to rank because the information is not sufficient to determine whether the matter is important or not. For example, if one of the options states: "A security guard contacts you and asks you to move your car as it is badly parked", then your ranking will be different depending on whether the car is stopping ambulances from accessing A&E, or whether it is just slightly sticking out in the normal car park.

If the car is blocking ambulance access and you are busy with an emergency, the best that you could do would be to give your keys to a colleague so that he could move the car for you, or to ask the colleague to take over from you so that you can go and move your own car. It would rank high on your list of tasks and you would be able to sort things out through suitable delegation.

If the car is just annoying a few visitors, then it would be the least of your priorities in relation to other more pressing matters; you would then prioritise it last.

The main problem is that you just don't know what the situation is. What matters though is that there is a risk that it may be in a dangerous place (patient safety is potentially affected). In this situation, you would therefore need to gain more information from the security guard, which would take 5 seconds (in fact a secretary could do it for you if you were busy) and you can then advise.

This is a case of a situation where a seemingly non-patient-related matter could potentially impact on patient care. Overall, it would therefore rank high, simply because of the potential risk to patients, and you would need to explain the dilemma that you face together with the need to use colleagues to sort the situation out.

Additional comments

It is unlikely that any comments written outside the boxes will be given any marks, but if you have time – and ONLY if you have time – there are a few additional comments that may be appropriate to write as a brief introduction and brief conclusion. Some of these comments could actually also be included in the main body of your justifications.

Comments that may be relevant include:

- Recognising that the task is difficult.

- Recognising that time is very limited.

- Recognising the need for further information.

- Recognising the need to utilise all members of the multidisciplinary team available to you including both clinical and non-clinical staff.

- Recognising the need to delegate where possible. This includes delegating down to junior colleagues, across to your peers, up to senior colleagues and to other members of the multidisciplinary team where appropriate.

- Stating what you would normally do in situations like that described. Examples would include writing a "to do" list or calling a colleague to help.

- Reviewing the workload and reprioritising where possible (i.e. once you have prioritised, circumstances might change and you need to remain adaptable to varying circumstances).

- Recognising the effect on you and the need for time out and debriefing, particularly after a stressful situation.

Assessment criteria

The prioritisation exercise is definitely testing your ability to solve problems, work under pressure of time, your professional probity, thought processes and personal organisation, your multidisciplinary team working skills and the effect upon you.

The marking schedule will therefore take account of a range of factors, including many from the list below:

273

1. **Written skills**
    If the assessor cannot read your writing, they will be unable to give you your mark. You will need to write quickly during this exercise.

    Try to make your handwriting as legible as you can. Practise at least one of the exercises that follow with the time limit applied. Look at your writing. Can you read it? Ask a colleague. Can they read it?

2. **Approach**
    Did you think about the tasks and messages before you started writing?
    Did you make any logical notes?
    Are there multiple scribbles on your paper because you changed your mind over and over again?

3. **Thought process**
    Is your thinking and justification clear?
    Does it make sense?
    Is it appropriate?
    Do you have multiple mistakes crossed out because you changed your mind?

4. **Emergency case**
    Did you recognise that there was a clinical case that needed urgent attention?
    Did you put the patient first?
    Are you a safe doctor?
    It is essential to deal with the clinical emergency as a first priority.

5. **Ranking**
    Did you rank the tasks as requested?
    Did you use the correct lettering/ numbering scheme?
    Is the ranking appropriate?
    Do the "patient-centred" tasks come before the "extended patient" tasks? Do the "other" tasks rank lower down?

6. **Teamwork**
    Did you use the team?
    Did you think about clinical and non-clinical members of the multidisciplinary team?
    Was the delegation appropriate?

Should you have completed more tasks yourself?
Did you state anywhere that you would check to see if the tasks had been completed and get follow-up from your team members?

7. **Time management**
   Did you complete the exercise?
   Did you leave time for the reflective learning (if present)?
   Are your answers to the first two stems very long with only a sentence for the other stems?
   Did you rush the last few stems?

8. **Effect on you**
   Did you acknowledge the effect that one or more of the tasks had on you, the person?
   Did you explain this in your answer?
   Was your ranking appropriate when taking into account the effect on you?

9. **Reflective learning**
   Did you leave enough time for the reflective learning?
   Did you complete all sections requested?
   Did you learn anything from the exercise?
   Were you open to the fact that we all make mistakes?
   Did you acknowledge your limitations?
   Did you appreciate what you did well?
   Is there anything that you would do differently next time after experiencing this exercise?
   Did you learn anything about yourself?

How to prepare for the day

Practise, practise, practise. Start by thinking about what you do in your everyday life, when you are at work and on call. How do you organise and prioritise your time and tasks? When you are at home, how do you juggle your home commitments such as childcare, cooking, shopping and cleaning with your social life and work life? What techniques do you employ?

Make sure that the way that you handle the written task reflects your own skills. Write down how *you* would prioritise, not how you think it should be prioritised or how this book (or others) tells you to prioritise.

Once you have thought about your own techniques, use the exercises in the book to practise. Make sure you do at least one example with a stopwatch and the added pressure of time. Write down the answers in full as you would do on the day and ask someone else to read them.

You will of course pick up some things by just reading through the exercises, but you will gain so much more by working through them under examination conditions.

The gold standard once again is to find a reputable and well-respected course that will allow you to practise with trained tutors. Make sure it has a focus on the written prioritisation exercise and has a small number of candidates. Listen to the feedback and learn from the other participants. See what works well and what doesn't. Use everything that you can to improve and prepare for the day.

Figure 10. Key assessment criteria for the written prioritisation exercise

1. Written skills
2. Approach
3. Thought process
4. Emergency case
5. Ranking
   - Patient
   - Extended Patient
   - Other
6. Teamwork
7. Time management
8. Effect on you
9. Reflective learning

L Task prioritisation Practice exercises

In this section, you will find examples of prioritisation exercises that you can use to practise.

If you simply read through the examples, you will pick up some information, but you will gain so much more by writing them out. To do this effectively, you need to allow yourself 30 minutes of uninterrupted time. Turn off your mobile phone, the radio and the television. Draw out a marking sheet with limited space for your answers or write in the spaces provided in the book, and only look at the question under a time pressured "examination" setting. Try to keep at least one of the following examples to practise in this way

Ask a colleague to look at your written answer after you have completed the exercise. Get them to mark you based on the criteria discussed above.

The preparation exercises

Each of the following exercises will try to recreate a type of question that you may get on the day. There is one type 1 (least common) prioritisation question just for practice, and the rest are type 2 (most common) examples. It is the type 2 example that you are more likely to get on the day.

The first 5 questions are explained in detail. These explanations are far more detailed than you will be expected (or able) to write within 30 minutes. They are exhaustive to show you what you "could" write given unlimited time. It is up to you to decide how much information you personably are able to write within the time limit.

There then follows 25 more exercises with less detailed explanations for practice.

Remember that there is no absolute right and wrong answer to how you rank the tasks. You must however ensure that you justify them appropriately and that you are a SAFE doctor.

Prioritisation 1 Exam paper

You are an SHO/F2 doctor based in A&E and have 1 hour left until the end of your 12-hour shift. There are normally two doctors covering each shift.

You have just returned to the department after escorting a patient to the intensive care unit when the senior nurse approaches you. She explains that the second doctor who should be covering the department has a severe migraine and has had to go and lie down. The senior nurse tells you that the department is very busy and she will try to find someone to help. She has written down a list of things that you need to do urgently.

You need to explain how you would proceed with each task, why you would respond in that particular way and then finally rank the order in which you would perform the tasks from A to F.

A is the first task that you would perform and F is the task that you would leave until last.

Messages

1. The Consultant from intensive care has called. He wants to speak to you about the patient that you have transferred to them. There are some notes missing from the patient file.

Ranking [   ]

2. As you are reading the list of messages you hear a nurse shouting for assistance in the resuscitation room. They are asking for the resuscitation trolley and defibrillator.

Ranking [   ]

>>>> Continues next page >>>>

3. A message has been left to call the nursery that your son attends.

Ranking

4. There is a patient waiting to see you in the "majors" area of A&E who is having a heavy PV bleed. The nurse has noted down the possibility of a miscarriage. Pregnancy test is positive.

Ranking

5. The blood bank technician has called. A "group and save" blood request that you sent through to them earlier is not labelled properly. They need you to go to the laboratory and confirm the patient details.

Ranking [ ]

6. An SHO / F2 doctor has called you and left a message for you to ring back about the mess party later that night.

Ranking [ ]

>>>> Continues next page >>>>

Reflective learning

1. What single thing did you find difficult about the exercise?

2. What two things did you find easy about the exercise?

3. What have you learnt from completing this exercise about yourself?

4. What one thing would you do differently next time?

Prioritisation 2   Exam paper

You are an F2/SHO doctor based in primary care. You are at the end of your 4-month attachment and the partners allow you to see patients independently, asking for help whenever you need it.

It is 11:00. The only other doctor in the surgery is a partner. The partner calls you stating that there is an emergency home visit that he is going to attend leaving you in the surgery alone. He aims to be back before the end of surgery at 12:00 to help you finish. He leaves.

The following tasks need completing.

Task 1   The receptionist calls you. A man has approached the desk and is angry that he is having to wait. His appointment was at 10:50. The receptionist states that he is shouting and threatening to complain.

Task 2   You have an appointment at the hospital to see a Consultant about your own health at 12:15. Your last patient had been booked in at 11:00, which would have given you time to get there.

Task 3   The practice nurse calls you. There is a patient having an acute asthma attack in her room. She requests your help.

Task 4   There is a telephone call from a patient. A wasp has stung her 2-year-old daughter. Her face has started to swell up. She is struggling to breathe.

Task 5   The senior practice nurse needs a prescription signing for some antibiotics. The patient is with her and is in a rush to leave.

Task 6   A drug representative is waiting to see you.

>>>> Continues next page >>>>

283

Justify how you would complete the tasks in the boxes below in the order that you would complete them. A is the first task that you would complete. F is the last task that you would complete.

A

Task: ☐

B

Task: ☐

C

Task: ☐

D

Task: [ ]

E

Task: [ ]

F

Task: [ ]

>>>> **Continues next page** >>>>

Reflective learning

1. What two things did you find difficult about the exercise?

2. What one thing did you find easy about the exercise?

3. What have you learnt from completing this exercise about yourself?

4. What two things would you do differently next time?

Prioritisation 3 Exam paper

You are a doctor based in primary care. You are at the end of your 4-month attachment and the partners allow you to see patients independently, asking for help whenever you need it.

It is Friday afternoon and there is one other doctor in the surgery. Your clinic list finishes early every Friday at 18:00 to allow you to attend an evening class. Today's class is the final one in the series before the summer holiday and you will receive your exam results.

It is now 16:45 and you still have a waiting room full of patients. You like to run to time. You receive 5 messages in succession.

1   The community Macmillan nurse calls. A terminal patient of yours needs to start a subcutaneous infusion of morphine. It has been agreed, but you need to write the prescription up and arrange for delivery to the house. The pharmacy closes at 17:00. The Macmillan nurse hands over to an on-call service at 17:00.

2   Your job application for specialist "run through" training is due to be submitted by the end of today. You still have some details to complete before sending it off by email.

3   The relative of a recently deceased patient has called asking for you to contact them about a request for a post-mortem examination by the coroner. Your colleague had reported the death to the coroner as the patient had died suddenly and had not seen a doctor recently.

4   The local pharmacist has called and would like to speak to you about a recent prescription that you have written.

5   There is a patient in reception who is waiting for a letter that you had promised to leave at reception by Friday afternoon at the latest. The receptionist calls to ask if you can write it now. The patient is agitated.

>>>> Continues next page >>>>

Justify how you would complete the tasks in the boxes below in the order that you would complete them. Remember that you need to leave to reach your class. A is the first task that you would complete. E is the last task that you would complete.

A

Message: ☐

B

Message: ☐

C

Message: ☐

D | **Message:** [ ]

E | **Message:** [ ]

Other comments

>>>> Continues next page >>>>

Reflective learning

1. What three things did you find difficult about the exercise?

2. What one thing did you find easy about the exercise?

3. What two things have you learnt about yourself from completing this exercise?

4. What two things would you do differently next time?

Prioritisation 4 Exam paper

You are a doctor based in A&E.

Rank the following tasks in the order that you would perform them.

1. A patient is having severe haematemesis and has collapsed with a blood pressure of 60/40.

2. A patient has died and the nurses want you to certify the death.

3. A stable elderly lady has been in A&E for 3 hours. She needs referral to the elderly care team. Her family keep asking the nurses when she will be moved.

4. You need to go to the library to pay a fine on an overdue book.

5. You need to take some blood gasses from a patient with pancreatitis. The surgeons are aware of the patient and you are awaiting their review.

>>>> Continues next page >>>>

Justify how you would complete the tasks in the boxes below in the order that you would complete them. A is the first task that you would complete. E is the last task that you would complete.

A

Task: [ ]

B

Task: [ ]

C

Task: [ ]

D

Task:

E

Task:

>>>> Continues next page >>>>

Reflective learning

1. What two things did you find difficult about the exercise?

2. What one thing did you find easy about the exercise?

3. What have you learnt from completing this exercise about yourself?

4. What two things would you do differently next time?

Prioritisation 5 Exam paper

Rank the following tasks in the order that you would perform them.

You are a surgical SHO/F2 doctor and on call.

1. You need to attend theatre to assist your Registrar with a routine appendectomy.

2. You have been asked to attend A&E to review an emergency patient with suspected ruptured AAA (abdominal aortic aneurysm).

3. A patient on ITU needs a surgical review for possible small bowel obstruction.

4. The Consultant on call has left a message for you to contact him. He is unable to reach the Registrar.

5. A ward patient needs to be reviewed prior to discharge. They are well.

>>>> Continues next page >>>>

Justify how you would complete the tasks in the boxes below in the order that you would complete them. A is the first task that you would complete. E is the last task that you would complete.

A
Task: [ ]

B
Task: [ ]

C
Task: [ ]

D

Task: ☐

E

Task: ☐

>>>> Continues next page >>>>

Reflective learning

1. What two things did you find difficult about the exercise?

2. What one thing did you find easy about the exercise?

3. What have you learnt from completing this exercise about yourself?

4. What two things would you do differently next time?

Prioritisation 6 Exam paper

(Prepare your own answer sheet based on the model used for the first 5 prioritisation exercises)

You are an F2/SHO doctor on call for medicine. Rank the following tasks in the order that you would perform them.

1. The coronary care unit (CCU) has called. They have a patient who needs to be seen. The nurses have noticed runs of ventricular tachycardia (VT) on the monitor. The patient appears well and has a pulse and good blood pressure.

2. The arrest bleep goes off. A call has been put out on the orthopaedic ward.

3. A patient wants to self-discharge from the ward. They are post-overdose and have been reviewed by Psychiatry as no further suicide risk.

4. A&E needs you to attend and review a young asthmatic. The patient is unwell and may need HDU.

5. The pharmacy needs you to contact them to double-check a patient's medication that you have written for discharge.

6. You need to buy you partner a birthday card. It's today and you've forgotten.

Justify how you would complete the tasks in the order that you would complete them. A is the first task that you would complete. F is the last task that you would complete.

Reflective learning
1. What two things did you find difficult about the exercise?
2. What one thing did you find easy about the exercise?
3. What have you learnt from completing this exercise about yourself?
4. What two things would you do differently next time?

Prioritisation 7 Exam paper

(Prepare your own answer sheet based on the model used for the first 5 prioritisation exercises)

You are an F2/SHO doctor covering the obstetrics and gynaecology on call. Rank the following tasks in the order that you would perform them.

1. There is a suspected ruptured ectopic pregnancy in A&E. You have been asked to attend.

2. You need to cancel your dentist appointment for tomorrow.

3. Your Registrar has called you. They are about to start a Caesarean section and would like you to assist.

4. An antenatal patient wants to be discharged and needs a letter.

5. You have to finish your audit project to present at the departmental meeting tomorrow morning.

6. A midwife calls for you urgently. A patient on labour ward is having a severe postpartum haemorrhage (PPH).

Justify how you would complete the tasks in the order that you would complete them. A is the first task that you would complete. F is the last task that you would complete.

Reflective learning
1. What two things did you find difficult about the exercise?
2. What one thing did you find easy about the exercise?
3. What have you learnt from completing this exercise about yourself?
4. What two things would you do differently next time?

Prioritisation 8 Exam paper

(Prepare your own answer sheet based on the model used for the first 5 prioritisation exercises)

You are an F2/SHO doctor in primary care. Rank the following tasks in the order that you would perform them.

1. You have just been asked to plan a teaching session for the medical students attached to the practice. The session starts in 2 hours.

2. The heath visitor is concerned about a child she has just seen in her clinic and would like to talk to you.

3. The practice manager needs to talk to you about the on-call rota.

4. The practice nurse has called. She would like some advice about a child who is due for their immunisation. The child is allergic to eggs and has severe eczema.

5. The receptionist calls. A patient is on the line, complaining of chest pain.

6. You mother has called, and left a message saying that your father is in hospital.

Justify how you would complete the tasks in the order that you would complete them. A is the first task that you would complete. F is the last task that you would complete.

Reflective learning
1. What two things did you find difficult about the exercise?
2. What one thing did you find easy about the exercise?
3. What have you learnt from completing this exercise about yourself?
4. What two things would you do differently next time?

Prioritisation 9 Exam paper

(Prepare your own answer sheet based on the model used for the first 5 prioritisation exercises)

You are an F2 doctor in obstetrics and gynaecology. It is 13:00 (1pm). Rank the following tasks in the order that you would perform them.

1. The registrar has called you to meet for a coffee so that you can both discuss the ward patients.

2. The labour ward has called you. They need IV access for a patient who is a routine admission.

3. A&E have called. A lady who is having a miscarriage needs to be admitted. She is stable but has chosen to be admitted because she lives alone.

4. The gynaecology ward need a patient reviewed. She is post op and has a blood pressure of 70/40. She is unresponsive.

5. You are rota organiser and you need to give the secretary the finalised rota to print by the end of the day.

6. You have not yet eaten lunch and want to go and buy something.

Justify how you would complete the tasks in the order that you would complete them. A is the first task that you would complete. F is the last task that you would complete.

Reflective learning
1. What two things did you find difficult about the exercise?
2. What one thing did you find easy about the exercise?
3. What have you learnt from completing this exercise about yourself?
4. What two things would you do differently next time?

Prioritisation 10 Exam paper

(Prepare your own answer sheet based on the model used for the first 5 prioritisation exercises)

You are an F2 doctor based in paediatrics. Rank the following tasks in the order that you would perform them.

1. Your routine ward round with your registrar started early. They expect you there straight away.

2. You need to take routine bloods from a jaundiced baby. Mum has just arrived in the day unit.

3. The labour ward have bleeped you; they are about to start a Caesarian section for twins and you are required to attend as the paediatrician on call.

4. You need to complete one of your assessments for foundation competencies. You are due to sit with your consultant and are already late.

5. A&E have called. A child with acute asthma, whom they have stabilised, requires admission.

Justify how you would complete the tasks in the order that you would complete them. A is the first task that you would complete. E is the last task that you would complete.

Reflective learning
1. What two things did you find difficult about the exercise?
2. What one thing did you find easy about the exercise?
3. What have you learnt from completing this exercise about yourself?
4. What two things would you do differently next time?

Prioritisation 11 Exam paper

(Prepare your own answer sheet based on the model used for the first 5 prioritisation exercises)

You are an F2 doctor in psychiatry. Rank the following tasks in the order that you would perform them.

1. The police have called. A patient they are escorting to the assessment unit needs to be seen. The patient is psychotic.

2. The ward need a routine drug chart rewritten.

3. The ward have a new routine patient who requires clerking and admission. The nurses cannot give them their medication until you have seen them.

4. You have a job application to send today and need to login to 'NHS jobs' to do this.

5. You have a teaching session with the occupational therapists tomorrow and need to complete your presentation.

6. You really need a coffee. You had a late night last night.

Justify how you would complete the tasks in the order that you would complete them. A is the first task that you would complete. F is the last task that you would complete.

Reflective learning
1. What two things did you find difficult about the exercise?
2. What one thing did you find easy about the exercise?
3. What have you learnt from completing this exercise about yourself?
4. What two things would you do differently next time?

Prioritisation 12 Exam paper

(Prepare your own answer sheet based on the model used for the first 5 prioritisation exercises)

You are an F2 doctor working in ENT. Rank the following tasks in the order that you would perform them.

1. The ward sister has called you to review a patient who is awaiting discharge. The patient are stable.

2. A&E have called. They want you to see an unstable patient with a severe nosebleed. The patient's blood pressure is 100/60.

3. The ward need a review of a post op patient following tonsillectomy. They are bleeding. Their blood pressure is 100/60.

4. Your sister called and left a message asking you to call her urgently.

5. Your car is parked in the main car park and your "pay and display" ticket is about to run out. You need to put more money in the meter.

6. The outpatient clinic is running late. They have requested that you go and help to speed things up.

Justify how you would complete the tasks in the order that you would complete them. A is the first task that you would complete. F is the last task that you would complete.

Reflective learning
1. What two things did you find difficult about the exercise?
2. What one thing did you find easy about the exercise?
3. What have you learnt from completing this exercise about yourself?
4. What two things would you do differently next time?

Prioritisation 13 Exam paper

(Prepare your own answer sheet based on the model used for the first 5 prioritisation exercises)

You are an F2 doctor based on General Practice. Rank the following tasks in the order that you would perform them.

1. You need to carry out a home visit for an elderly lady in a nursing home with a temperature.

2. You need to carry out a home visit for a patient with end stage renal failure. They have diarrhoea.

3. You need to carry out a home visit to certify a patient's death.

4. The practice manager wants to talk to you about your pay. There has been a mistake in the tax calculation.

5. The practice partnership meeting is about to commence. You are expected to be there.

Justify how you would complete the tasks in the order that you would complete them. A is the first task that you would complete. E is the last task that you would complete.

Reflective learning
1. What two things did you find difficult about the exercise?
2. What one thing did you find easy about the exercise?
3. What have you learnt from completing this exercise about yourself?
4. What two things would you do differently next time?

Prioritisation 14 Exam paper

(Prepare your own answer sheet based on the model used for the first 5 prioritisation exercises)

You are an F2 in general medicine. Rank the following tasks in the order that you would perform them.

1. You are due to meet with your educational supervisor to discuss your career options in 5 minutes.

2. The arrest bleep goes off.

3. A&E are calling you, they have an 86-year-old who is "off legs" to be admitted.

4. A GP has requested you call them back to discuss a patient who was discharged last week.

5. The ward request some analgesia for a patient who has a head injury.

6. The ward request a review of a disturbed patient. They want a sedative prescribing.

Justify how you would complete the tasks in the order that you would complete them. A is the first task that you would complete. F is the last task that you would complete.

Reflective learning
1. What two things did you find difficult about the exercise?
2. What one thing did you find easy about the exercise?
3. What have you learnt from completing this exercise about yourself?
4. What two things would you do differently next time?

Prioritisation 15 Exam paper

(Prepare your own answer sheet based on the model used for the first 5 prioritisation exercises)

You are an F2 in general surgery. You have 6 patients in A&E waiting to be seen. The information you have on the patients is as follows. Rank the following tasks in the order that you would perform them.

1. A 36-year-old man with right iliac fossa pain. His observations are stable.

2. An 86-year-old smoker, with severe pain in his abdomen radiating through to his back. His blood pressure is 90/40.

3. A 24-year-old trauma patient with multiple injuries bought in by paramedics to A&E majors. The A&E team are still with him.

4. A 64-year-old with chronic constipation.

5. A 5-year-old with a one week history of abdominal pain. He is apyrexial.

6. A 47-year-old referred by the GP with suspected small bowel obstruction (SBO). He is dehydrated but his observations are normal.

Justify how you would complete the tasks in the order that you would complete them. A is the first task that you would complete. F is the last task that you would complete.

Reflective learning
1. What two things did you find difficult about the exercise?
2. What one thing did you find easy about the exercise?
3. What have you learnt from completing this exercise about yourself?
4. What two things would you do differently next time?

Prioritisation 16 Exam paper

(Prepare your own answer sheet based on the model used for the first 5 prioritisation exercises)

You are an F2 in General Practice. You have returned from lunch to 6 messages. Rank the following tasks in the order that you would perform them.

1. A 6-year-old boy whom you saw this morning needs his antibiotics changing. You prescribed the wrong ones.

2. A well-known patient of yours has called and asked you to visit her at home. She is usually well and just needs her new prescription when she asks for a visit.

3. An A&E doctor has called. Can you contact them regarding one of your patients who has been admitted. They need more information.

4. Your partner called. Please call them as soon as you can.

5. The payroll/wages department at the primary care trust (PCT) has called. Can you call them back urgently?

6. The F2 who is replacing you at the end of your attachment in General Practice has called. They would like to chat about the job.

Justify how you would complete the tasks in the order that you would complete them. A is the first task that you would complete. F is the last task that you would complete.

Reflective learning
1. What two things did you find difficult about the exercise?
2. What one thing did you find easy about the exercise?
3. What have you learnt from completing this exercise about yourself?
4. What two things would you do differently next time?

Prioritisation 17 Exam paper

(Prepare your own answer sheet based on the model used for the first 5 prioritisation exercises)

You are an F2 in elderly care medicine. It is 15:00 (3pm). Rank the following tasks in the order that you would perform them.

1. A 92-year-old patient has fallen out of bed. The nurses are worried about a fractured neck of femur.

2. An 86-year-old patient has vomited twice in the last 12 hours. They need an antiemetic.

3. You need a coffee. You have not had a drink all day.

4. A 76-year-old patient has a headache and needs some paracetamol.

5. There is a new admission to be seen. They have been transferred from A&E to the ward and are stable.

6. You need to pay your GMC (General Medical Council) membership fees. They are due today.

Justify how you would complete the tasks in the order that you would complete them. A is the first task that you would complete. F is the last task that you would complete.

Reflective learning
1. What two things did you find difficult about the exercise?
2. What one thing did you find easy about the exercise?
3. What have you learnt from completing this exercise about yourself?
4. What two things would you do differently next time?

Prioritisation 18 Exam paper

(Prepare your own answer sheet based on the model used for the first 5 prioritisation exercises)

You are an F2 based in Obstetrics and gynaecology (O&G). Rank the following tasks in the order that you would perform them.

1. You need to renew your car insurance. You drive to work and it expires today.

2. There is an emergency call to labour ward. There is a lady having a post partum haemorrhage.

3. The antenatal ward need 4 drug charts rewriting.

4. The postnatal ward need you to discharge 3 women as they need to move people out of labour ward into those beds urgently.

5. Labour ward have asked for a review of a postnatal women with a temperature

6. A&E have called. There is a suspected ectopic pregnancy in A&E. The patient is currently stable.

Justify how you would complete the tasks in the order that you would complete them. A is the first task that you would complete. F is the last task that you would complete.

Reflective learning
1. What two things did you find difficult about the exercise?
2. What one thing did you find easy about the exercise?
3. What have you learnt from completing this exercise about yourself?
4. What two things would you do differently next time?

Prioritisation 19 Exam paper

(Prepare your own answer sheet based on the model used for the first 5 prioritisation exercises)

You are an F2 in general medicine. Rank the following tasks in the order that you would perform them.

1. A GP referral is waiting with a suspected subarachnoid haemorrhage.

2. A GP referral "off legs" is waiting to be seen. The 86-year-old is stable.

3. The crash bleep starts sounding.

4. A fellow F2 has called and asked you to swap this weekend on call with her; she is visiting her mother who is sick. Can you call her urgently to let her know?

5. There is a message on your mobile phone from your bank. Can you call the fraud investigation unit as soon as possible.

6. An A&E referral with an infective exacerbation of COPD (Chronic Obstructive Pulmonary disease) is awaiting review. The patient has been stabilised and is currently well with saturations of 96% on air.

Justify how you would complete the tasks in the order that you would complete them. A is the first task that you would complete. F is the last task that you would complete.

Reflective learning
1. What two things did you find difficult about the exercise?
2. What one thing did you find easy about the exercise?
3. What have you learnt from completing this exercise about yourself?
4. What two things would you do differently next time?

Prioritisation 20 Exam paper

(Prepare your own answer sheet based on the model used for the first 5 prioritisation exercises)

You are an F2 in emergency medicine. It is 09:00am. Rank the following tasks in the order that you would perform them.

1. A nurse practitioner has asked for your help to suture a scalp laceration. It has stopped bleeding and the patient is stable.

2. The A&E receptionists are querying an entry you made in some patient notes yesterday. They want to talk to you.

3. Your consultant has asked for you to collate some notes for an audit meeting. She needs them by lunchtime.

4. The emergency alarm is sounding. There is a problem in majors.

5. A paediatric patient with suspected tonsillitis is waiting to be seen. They have a temperature of 38 °C.

6. There is a closed stable ankle fracture that you need to put in a cast.

Justify how you would complete the tasks in the order that you would complete them. A is the first task that you would complete. F is the last task that you would complete.

Reflective learning
1. What two things did you find difficult about the exercise?
2. What one thing did you find easy about the exercise?
3. What have you learnt from completing this exercise about yourself?
4. What two things would you do differently next time?

Prioritisation 21 Exam paper

(Prepare your own answer sheet based on the model used for the first 5 prioritisation exercises)

You are an F2 doctor in general medicine. There are 6 referrals you need to see. Rank the following tasks in the order that you would perform them.

1. An 81-year-old with mild shortness of breath. Their saturations on air are 99%.

2. An 18-year-old with an attempted suicide. The GP said the patient drank a bottle of vodka and scratched her wrists with a razor. No medication was taken and there is no deep laceration to the wrist. Her observations are stable but she is vomiting.

3. An 18-year-old with insulin dependent diabetes was found collapsed at home with a blood sugar of 1. There are now awake with a blood sugar of 5 and feel well.

4. An 18-year-old with insulin dependent diabetes and a chest infection has a blood sugar of 36. There are ketones in the urine.

5. A 65-year-old with suspected DVT following a long haul flight. They are well.

6. A 45-year-old with end stage ovarian cancer and has been admitted for pain control. The palliative care nurse gave them oral morphine before sending them into hospital and they are currently pain free.

Justify how you would complete the tasks in the order that you would complete them. A is the first task that you would complete. F is the last task that you would complete.

Reflective learning
1. What two things did you find difficult about the exercise?
2. What one thing did you find easy about the exercise?
3. What have you learnt from completing this exercise about yourself?
4. What two things would you do differently next time?

Prioritisation 22 | Exam paper

(Prepare your own answer sheet based on the model used for the first 5 prioritisation exercises)

You are an F2 based in primary care. Rank the following tasks in the order that you would perform them.

1. You need to move your car from the car park. You are taking the practice manager's parking space currently and they are due to return in 15 minutes.

2. You need to call your builder. You are having work done to the house and have to tell them about colour schemes.

3. A known asthmatic has presented to the surgery. They are short of breath and unable to tell the receptionist their name.

4. The practice nurse wants you to review a rash on a child. The child is apyrexial.

5. A patient has called for advice. Their 3-year-old has been vomiting for 2 days and has not been able to drink anything this morning.

6. You have a pile of repeat prescriptions to sign.

Justify how you would complete the tasks in the order that you would complete them. A is the first task that you would complete. F is the last task that you would complete.

Reflective learning
1. What two things did you find difficult about the exercise?
2. What one thing did you find easy about the exercise?
3. What have you learnt from completing this exercise about yourself?
4. What two things would you do differently next time?

Prioritisation 23 Exam paper

(Prepare your own answer sheet based on the model used for the first 5 prioritisation exercises)

You are an F2 in radiology. It is 09:00am. Rank the following tasks in the order that you would perform them.

1. You are due to sit in with your consultant to observe an interventional procedure that starts in 10 minutes.

2. CT (computerised tomography) scanning have asked for you to review a patient who has had a contrast CT and had an adverse reaction to the contrast. The patient is asthmatic.

3. A patient who is due to have a barium enema is vomiting. The radiographer wants you to review them to see if they can proceed.

4. You need to book an ultrasound for a patient with suspected pancreatitis. The on call medical team called you 25 minutes ago. The patient is unstable and in A&E.

5. You need to call home. You think you left the iron on this morning.

6. You have 30 routine chest x-rays to report. You are due to sit with your supervisor over lunchtime to review them.

Justify how you would complete the tasks in the order that you would complete them. A is the first task that you would complete. F is the last task that you would complete.

Reflective learning
1. What two things did you find difficult about the exercise?
2. What one thing did you find easy about the exercise?
3. What have you learnt from completing this exercise about yourself?
4. What two things would you do differently next time?

Prioritisation 24 Exam paper

(Prepare your own answer sheet based on the model used for the first 5 prioritisation exercises)

You are an F2 in general medicine. Rank the following tasks in the order that you would perform them.

1. The arrest bleep is sounding

2. A patient has collapsed on the ward. The nurses have put them into bed. They are conscious but in pain. BP 122/78 HR 95 Saturations 100%

3. A patient has arrived in A&E with massive haematemesis. You have been fast bleeped to attend.

4. Your F1 has asked for you to review a patient that they are unable to insert an IV (intravenous) line into.

5. The admissions ward have requested you to review 3 GP admissions

6. You need to update your Facebook® profile.

Justify how you would complete the tasks in the order that you would complete them. A is the first task that you would complete. F is the last task that you would complete.

Reflective learning
1. What two things did you find difficult about the exercise?
2. What one thing did you find easy about the exercise?
3. What have you learnt from completing this exercise about yourself?
4. What two things would you do differently next time?

Prioritisation 25 Exam paper

(Prepare your own answer sheet based on the model used for the first 5 prioritisation exercises)

You are an F2 in general surgery. It is 08:30am. Rank the following tasks in the order that you would perform them.

1. You need to collate the patient notes for the X-ray meeting at lunchtime.

2. You have blood test request forms to complete before the phlebotomist arrives on the ward at 09:00am.

3. A patient on the ward requires IV access. Their antibiotics were due at 06:00am.

4. You need your morning coffee. You were late this morning and did not have one at home.

5. Sister on the ward wants to task to you about a patient who was disruptive over night

6. 3 drug charts need rewriting prior to the nurses drug round at 10:00am.

Justify how you would complete the tasks in the order that you would complete them. A is the first task that you would complete. F is the last task that you would complete.

Reflective learning
1. What two things did you find difficult about the exercise?
2. What one thing did you find easy about the exercise?
3. What have you learnt from completing this exercise about yourself?
4. What two things would you do differently next time?

Prioritisation 26 Exam paper

(Prepare your own answer sheet based on the model used for the first 5 prioritisation exercises)

You are an F2 in primary care. It is 09:00am. Rank the following tasks in the order that you would perform them.

1. Your first patient has arrived. Their appointment is at 09:00am.

2. You have a pile of repeat prescriptions to be completed.

3. You have a telephone message asking you to call a patient you saw yesterday to arrange another appointment. They want to see you today urgently.

4. The practice manager wants to talk to you. Your CPR (cardiopulmonary resuscitation) training is overdue and they want to arrange training for you.

5. There is a home visit request from a 24-year-old with gastroenteritis. They are still drinking fluids.

6. There is a home visit request from a 96-year-old who requires a routine review and update of her medications.

Justify how you would complete the tasks in the order that you would complete them. A is the first task that you would complete. F is the last task that you would complete.

Reflective learning
1. What two things did you find difficult about the exercise?
2. What one thing did you find easy about the exercise?
3. What have you learnt from completing this exercise about yourself?
4. What two things would you do differently next time?

Prioritisation 27 Exam paper

(Prepare your own answer sheet based on the model used for the first 5 prioritisation exercises)

You are an F2 in General Practice. It is the last day of your attachment. You leave in 2 hours. Rank the following tasks in the order that you would perform them.

1. You are expected in the kitchen area for your leaving celebration in 1 hour.

2. You need to clear out your room of all your personal belongings.

3. You have 3 letters to dictate for referrals to secondary care.

4. You need to chase up an urgent blood test from a jaundiced patient you saw earlier today. Depending on the result, you may need to refer them to the medical team on call.

5. There is a telephone message asking for an insurance report to be completed. The patient will need a full medical examination.

6. There is a telephone message from your partner; can you call them at some point.

Justify how you would complete the tasks in the order that you would complete them. A is the first task that you would complete. F is the last task that you would complete.

Reflective learning
1. What two things did you find difficult about the exercise?
2. What one thing did you find easy about the exercise?
3. What have you learnt from completing this exercise about yourself?
4. What two things would you do differently next time?

Prioritisation 28 | Exam paper

(Prepare your own answer sheet based on the model used for the first 5 prioritisation exercises)

You are an F2 in orthopaedics. Rank the following tasks in the order that you would perform them.

1. You are expected to assist in a total hip replacement in 30 minutes. The consultant and registrar are both in theatre waiting for you.

2. You have a patient in A&E with a fractured ankle, who requires admission. He is stable but need to be prepared for theatre.

3. There is a child in the paediatric admissions unit with hip pain. The GP has suggested this may be irritable hip. You need to see and assess the child.

4. The ward nurses are requesting 5 drug charts to be rewritten.

5. The phlebotomist is unable to attend today. There are 6 sets of post-operative blood tests that need to be taken.

6. The trauma alert bleep has sounded. There is a major trauma about to arrive in A&E. You are expected to attend.

Justify how you would complete the tasks in the boxes below in the order that you would complete them. A is the first task that you would complete. F is the last task that you would complete.

Reflective learning
1. What two things did you find difficult about the exercise?
2. What one thing did you find easy about the exercise?
3. What have you learnt from completing this exercise about yourself?
4. What two things would you do differently next time?

Prioritisation 29 Exam paper

(Prepare your own answer sheet based on the model used for the first 5 prioritisation exercises)

You are an F2 in General Practice. Rank the following tasks in the order that you would perform them.

1. Your car is on a parking meter. It runs out in 15 minutes.

2. A man is on the telephone. He has chest pain.

3. There is a home visit request for a child with a fever and a rash.

4. You have 2 routine letters to dictate from your morning clinic.

5. You have forgotten your parents wedding anniversary and need to call them.

6. You need to call a patient to inform them of some test results. The tests are normal.

Justify how you would complete the tasks in the order that you would complete them. A is the first task that you would complete. F is the last task that you would complete.

Reflective learning
1. What two things did you find difficult about the exercise?
2. What one thing did you find easy about the exercise?
3. What have you learnt from completing this exercise about yourself?
4. What two things would you do differently next time?

Prioritisation 30 Exam paper

(Prepare your own answer sheet based on the model used for the first 5 prioritisation exercises)

You are an F2 in general medicine. Rank the following tasks in the order that you would perform them.

1. There is an acute asthmatic in A&E. They have a silent chest.

2. The gastroenterology ward are calling you. There is a patient having a massive haematemesis. The registrar is unavailable.

3. The arrest bleep is sounding.

4. An elderly care patient has become aggressive and the nurses need help.

5. A patient with a paracetamol overdose is in A&E and needs admitting.

6. You need to go to the toilet desperately.

Justify how you would complete the tasks in the order that you would complete them. A is the first task that you would complete. F is the last task that you would complete.

Reflective learning
1. What two things did you find difficult about the exercise?
2. What one thing did you find easy about the exercise?
3. What have you learnt from completing this exercise about yourself?
4. What two things would you do differently next time?

M Task prioritisation Discussions

Prioritisation 1 Exam paper

Read the brief

Did you spend time reading the brief?
Who are you?
Where are you based?
What job are you doing?
How much time do you have left on your shift?
Who is available to help you?

You know that you are working in A&E and therefore have a whole team of people to help out. This will include doctors from other specialities, nurses, and clerical staff amongst many others.

Who could you use to help with each task?

Task 1
Perhaps the receptionist or A&E "ward clerk" could help with the missing notes. They could contact ITU and find out exactly what is missing. It may be a simple case of the X-rays not being transferred with the patient. It could also be that the notes that are missing are the handwritten notes that you wrote after seeing the patient.

By writing in your justification:

I always complete my handwritten notes before moving on to the next patient; so any notes that are missing must be in the A&E department somewhere.

you would easily be able to justify delegating the finding and transportation of these notes to ITU to a member of the team. This would leave you free to complete the clinical tasks.

Task 2

If a nurse is shouting for help in an arrest situation and you are the only doctor in the department, you must complete this task yourself. Once you get to the arrest, things may change. When the medical or anaesthetic staff arrive, you could ask to leave the arrest team if appropriate.

Task 3

You could delegate this to a member of the non-clinical team to contact the nursery on your behalf to get more information about your son whilst you dealt with the emergency clinical cases. By asking the nominated member of your team to find you as soon as they have more information, you will ensure that you receive the information as quickly as you possibly can. Once you know what the problem is, you can then deal with it appropriately.

Task 4

There is already a nurse present with this patient; however, they are asking for your help with a PV bleed. It is important to support your team and so would be essential for a doctor to attend. You can either do this yourself, or ask the nurse to contact the on-call gynaecology team explaining about the case and the fact that there is only one doctor in the department and asking for their help until you are free to attend.

Task 5

The failure to label a blood bank form adequately is your responsibility. You will need to go to the lab yourself to complete the details. If you are unable to attend the blood bank and the patient needs a cross match for blood transfusion soon, there are two options.

    a.   You could ask the nurses/ phlebotomist to re-bleed the patient.
    b.   An alternative would be to ask a member of your team to go to the blood bank to retrieve the sample and bring it to you in the A&E department.

Task 6

This sounds like a personal call and you should therefore return the call yourself.

More information required

In all cases where messages of this type are left, we would always need to ascertain more information. This should be added to your justification.

Task 1
Before dealing with the missing notes I would ask the ward clerk to call ITU and find out exactly what notes were missing to enable me to deal with this task swiftly and efficiently.

Task 2
I would attend the arrest call immediately. This is an emergency and would need my urgent attention. Once present, depending on the clinical case and other team members present, I may or may not need to stay for the duration of the arrest.

Task 3
I need to know exactly what the problem with my son is before making a decision on how to proceed. I would ask the ward clerk/ nurse to call the nursery while I attended the arrest to ask what the problem was.

Task 4
To assess the clinical urgency of this case I would need more information. The nurse is asking for my help and so I would ensure that I attended as soon as I could. To decide how soon to attend, I would ask the attending nurse for more information. How many weeks pregnant is the woman? If she was 20 weeks pregnant or more, our local hospital policy is to transfer the woman to the antenatal ward. How heavily is she bleeding? What are her vital signs? (BP, HR, respiratory rate). Does she have a venflon and an intravenous infusion? How much pain is she in?

Task 5
I would want to know the urgency of this "group and save" sample. I would hope that I would remember the patient and be able to make a rapid decision as to whether this task could wait until I had completed the more urgent clinical cases.

Task 6
The mess party call could wait until I had completed all other tasks.

The assessment criteria

Remember the assessment criteria? (See Figure 10, page 276)

1 – Written skills
If the assessor cannot read your writing, they will be unable to give you the marks that you deserve.

Look at your writing. Can you read it?
Is it clear? Do you understand what you have written down?
Ask a colleague. Can they read it?

2 – Approach
Did you think about the tasks and messages before you started writing?
Did you make any logical notes?
Are there multiple scribbles on your paper because you changed your mind over and over again?
What could you do differently next time?

If you didn't make notes, try making them during the next practice exercise. You may find that it helps.
If you did make notes, did they help? Did they confuse you? Did you waste precious time writing them?

3 – Thought process
Is your thinking and justification clear?
Does it make sense? Is it appropriate?
Cross-check your justification with the ranking that you gave them.

Did you cross out multiple mistakes because you changed your mind?
What would you do differently next time?
Is there something you could do to help clarify your thoughts?

Did you try splitting the messages into "patient", "extended patient" and "other"?

"Patient"

2. As you are reading the list of messages you hear a nurse shouting for assistance in the resuscitation room. They are asking for the resuscitation trolley and defibrillator.

4. There is a patient waiting to see you in the "majors" area of A&E who is having a heavy PV bleed. The nurse has noted down the possibility of a miscarriage. Pregnancy test is positive.

"Extended patient"

1. The Consultant from intensive care has called. He wants to speak to you about the patient that you have transferred to them. There are some notes missing from the patient file.

5. The blood bank technician has called. A "group and save" blood request that you sent through to them earlier is not labelled properly. They need you to go to the laboratory and confirm the patient details.

"Other"

3. A message has been left to call the nursery that your son attends.

6. An F2/SHO doctor has called you and left a message for you to ring back about the mess party later that night.

By splitting the six messages into these categories it often helps to clarify the general order that the messages should be ranked into.

4 – The emergency case

Did you recognise that there was a clinical case that needed urgent attention?

In this list of messages the shout for help from the nurse with the arrest call would be your first and most urgent priority.

Did you put the patient first as suggested in the GMC guidance?
Are you a safe doctor?

5 – Ranking

Did you rank the tasks as requested?
Did you use the correct lettering scheme?

The brief stated that you should use A-F with A being the first priority and F being the least priority case. Did you follow this?

Is your ranking appropriate?
Do the "patient-centred" tasks come before the "extended patient" tasks?
Do the "other" tasks rank lower down?

The one exception to this may be the telephone call about your son and the effect on you. This "other" task may have ranked higher than an "extended patient" or even a "patient" task depending on your justification.

Suggested ranking

Assuming that a call from your son's nursery did not affect you at all, the ranking you decided upon is likely to be one of the following:

1	2	
A 2	A 2	Message 2 must come first as it is an arrest situation.
B 4	B 4	Message 4 is an urgent clinical case and should come second.
C 5	C 1	Message 1 from the ITU about the missing notes is important to deal with as it will indirectly affect a patient's care. Message 5 from the blood bank is also important to deal with, as this again will directly or indirectly affect patient care.
D 1	D 5	
		The order in which you choose to rank messages 1 and 5 will depend on how you choose to justify your choice.
E 3	E 3	Making the unlikely assumption that message 3 (the phone call about your son) would not affect you at all would place this lower down in the ranking. This is still more important than a social call about a mess party and so message 6 would definitely rank lowest at F.
F 6	F 6	

Remember that there is no absolute answer. If you allocated a greater weight to the phone call about your son then your ranking and justifications would be different. See later for a suggested approach.

6 – Teamwork

Did you use the team?

Did you think about clinical and non-clinical members of the multidisciplinary team?

Was the delegation appropriate?
Should you have completed more tasks yourself?
Should you have completed fewer tasks yourself?

Did you state anywhere that you would check to see if the tasks had been completed and get follow-up from your team members?

7 – Time management

Did you complete the exercise?
Did you leave time for the reflective learning?

Are your answers to the first two stems very long with only a sentence for the other stems? Did you rush the last few stems?

Did you have time to make a clear decision on the ranking or did you feel rushed into it?
How would you allocate the time better if you had to run the exercise again? Is there a better way?

8 – Effect on you

Did you acknowledge that the telephone call about your son in message 3 would have an effect on you, the person?

Did you explain this in your answer?

The nursery never calls me about my son at work unless something is seriously wrong. I would not be able to concentrate until I knew he was OK.

Justifying your answer in this way would allow you to place this "other" task much higher on your list of priorities. I do not think that you could justify putting it above the arrest call as this is a major emergency, but you could easily justify putting it second or third in the list.

The only way in which you could justify prioritising the call about your son as the first task on your list is if you delegated the phone call to someone else. For example, by stating that you would quickly ask the ward clerk (who was sitting at the desk in front of you) to contact the nursery and come to find you at the arrest call if your son was in any danger, you would be able to handle both your son and the arrest call as top priorities.

Was your ranking appropriate when taking into account the effect on you? Other possible ranking, recognising that message 3 would have an effect on you and how you would work, includes the following:

If you wanted to deal with your son first		If you dealt with the arrest call first and then your son		If you dealt with all the "patient" tasks first and then your son	
A 3	A 3	A 2	A 2	A 2	A 2
B 2	B 2	B 3	B 3	B 4	B 4
C 4	C 4	C 4	C 4	C 3	C 3
D 5	D 1	D 5	D 1	D 5	D 1
E 1	E 5	E 1	E 5	E 1	E 5
F 6	F 6	F 6	F 6	F 6	F 6

As you can see, your justification influences your ranking significantly. However, there is a general order of ranking that must be adhered to.

9 – Reflective learning

Did you leave enough time for the reflective learning?
Did you complete all sections requested?
Did you give the correct number of examples for each section?
Did you learn anything from the exercise?
Were you open to the fact that we all make mistakes?
Did you acknowledge your limitations?
Did you appreciate what you did well?
Is there anything that you would do differently next time after experiencing this exercise?
Did you learn anything about yourself?

Prioritisation 2 Discussion

Read the brief

Did you spend time reading the brief?
Who are you?
Where are you based?
What job are you doing?
How much time do you have left on your shift?

Who is available to help you?

You know that you are working in General Practice. You know that you are the only doctor, but have with you the rest of the General Practice team. The brief mentions a senior nurse, a nurse and a receptionist. There are often other people present in General Practice.

Is there a medical student?
Does the practice have a pharmacist, counsellor or other allied staff?
Is there another doctor/ partner who you could call in?
Is the partner that left on the telephone?
We tend to carry mobile phones with us. Could you call the partner?
What about the practice manager?

Who could you use to help with each task?

Task 1
The angry patient is only running 10 minutes late for his appointment. You could ask the receptionist if they would explain to all the patients waiting about the emergency and apologise for any delay. You could ask them to put up a sign. You could ask them to offer another appointment to any patient who feels that they have a non-urgent case and could wait for another day.

Task 2
It is important that you look after your own health. The GMC's *Good Medical Practice* states that you must be registered with a GP and acknowledge and recognise any ill health in yourself. You must try to attend this appointment.

You could ask if there is another partner at home who could come in and cover; you could also telephone the partner on the home visit explaining that you need to leave and asking them to come back as soon as they can.

The best person to help in this situation is the practice manager. Contact them and explain the need for you to leave and the exceptional situation that you are in. Ask for his or her help to find someone to cover for you if the partner is not back in time.

Task 3
The patient having an acute asthma attack will need your input. The brief states in task 5 that there is a senior nurse in the practice. Could you ask her to help? Can the nurses set up and give nebulisers? Asking for the nurse's help will allow you to attend to the patient but you will not necessarily have to stay with them. This will allow you to attend to other tasks.

Task 4
This sounds like it could be an anaphylactic reaction and so you will need to deal with this quickly. The child may need intramuscular adrenaline. The parent should be told to call the paramedics immediately. It is often quicker (unless you are a rural GP) to send the paramedics rather than visit the patient or get the parents to bring the child to the surgery.

Task 5
The prescription will need signing and, if you know the patient, their allergies and sensitivities will be quick to complete. You can ask the nurse to help explain to the patient the problem in the surgery and, if the patient has to leave, you could suggest that they leave the prescription and return later to pick it up once it has been signed.

Task 6
You could ask the receptionist to explain to the drug rep that you have been held up, suggesting an alternative appointment.

More information required

In all cases where messages of this type are left we would always need to ascertain more information. This should be added to your justification.

Task 1
No further information is required. You may wish to know how many patients are waiting and how many are non-urgent and willing to rebook an appointment for another day.

Task 2
You may wish to call the hospital clinic and explain that you may be late. Is the clinic running on time? Would the Consultant still see you if you turned up late?

Task 3
You would need to know information about the patient. How old are they? Are they a known asthmatic? What are their respiratory rate, blood pressure, heart rate and peak flow? Can they talk in sentences? Can the nurse give nebulisers?

Task 4
How far away is the patient? If she lives next door to the practice then her mum could bring her straight in. Otherwise, the paramedics would be quicker to respond.

Task 5
No further information is required.

Task 6
No further information is required.

The assessment criteria

Remember the assessment criteria? (See Figure 10, page 276)

1 – Written skills
If the assessor cannot read your writing, they will be unable to give you the marks that you deserve.

Look at your writing. Can you read it?
Is it clear? Do you understand what you have written down?
Ask a colleague. Can they read it?

2 – Approach

Did you think about the tasks and messages before you started writing?

Did you make any logical notes?

Are there multiple scribbles on your paper because you changed your mind over and over again?

What could you do differently next time?

If you didn't make notes, try making them during the next practice exercise. You may find that it helps. If you did make notes, did they help?

Did they confuse you? Did you waste precious time writing them?

3 – Thought process

Is your thinking and justification clear?

Does it make sense?

Is it appropriate?

Cross-check your justification with the ranking that you gave them.

Did you cross out multiple mistakes because you changed your mind? What would you do differently next time?

Is there something you could do to help clarify your thoughts?

Did you try splitting the messages into "patient", "extended patient" and "other"?

"Patient"

Task 3: The practice nurse calls you. There is a patient having an acute asthma attack in her room. She requests your help.

Task 4: There is a telephone call from a patient. A wasp has stung her 2-year-old daughter. Her face has started to swell up. She is struggling to breathe.

"Extended patient"

Task 1: The receptionist calls you. There are many patients in the waiting room to be seen. One man has approached the desk and is angry that he has to wait. His appointment was at 10:50. The receptionist states that he is shouting and threatening to complain.

Task 5: The senior practice nurse needs a prescription signing for some antibiotics. The patient is with her and is in a rush to leave.

"Other"

Task 2: You have an appointment at the hospital to see a Consultant about your own health at 12:15. Your last patient had been booked in at 11:00, which would have given you time to get there.

Task 6: A drug representative is waiting to see you.

By splitting the six messages into these categories it often helps to clarify the general order that the messages should be ranked into.

4 – The emergency case

Did you recognise that there were two clinical cases that needed urgent attention?
Both the acute asthma attack and the possible anaphylaxis need immediate attention. The telephone call about the anaphylaxis is likely to be very quick. Perhaps this should be ranked first?

Did you put the patient first as suggested in the GMC guidance?
Are you a safe doctor?

5 – Ranking

Did you rank the tasks as requested?

Did you place the first task in box A and the last task in box F?
How did you fill them in?

Did you decide on the obvious last and clear first task and then fill in the other boxes?
Did you fill in the boxes in order?

Whichever way you tried, did it work for you? Is it worth trying the exercise again approaching it in a different way?

Is your ranking appropriate?

Do the "patient-centred" tasks come before the "extended patient" tasks?
Do the "other" tasks rank lower down?

The one exception to this is task 2. You have an appointment about your own health, which you need to attend. Did you recognise the effect on you?

This "other" task should definitely have ranked higher than the drug rep and may have ranked higher than an "extended patient".

Suggested ranking

A 4   Both 4 and 3 are "patient" tasks. It doesn't really matter which
B 3   order you place these two cases in as long as they are in A and B. Both need your urgent clinical attention.

C 1   Both 1 and 5 are "extended patient" tasks. It doesn't matter
D 5   which order you place them in. I would suggest that they should be in C and D. They will both be reasonably quick to resolve with help.

E 2   Both 2 and 6 are "other" tasks. The drug rep is definitely the
F 6   least important, but we must recognise that we need to respect our colleagues and apologise to the drug rep.

Remember that there is no absolute answer. See below for an alternative answer when you recognise the effect of some of the tasks on you.

6 – Teamwork
Did you use the team?
Did you think about clinical and non-clinical members of the multidisciplinary team? Was the delegation appropriate?
Should you have completed more tasks yourself?
Should you have completed fewer tasks yourself?
Did you state anywhere that you would check to see if the tasks had been completed and get follow-up from your team members?

7 – Time management

Did you complete the exercise?

Did you leave time for the reflective learning?

Are your answers to the first two stems very long with only a sentence for the other stems?

Did you rush the last few stems?

Did you have time to make a clear decision on the ranking or did you feel rushed into it?

How would you allocate the time better if you had to run the exercise again? Is there a better way?

8 – Effect on you

Did you acknowledge that the need to leave on time to attend an appointment yourself would have an effect on you, the person?

Did you explain this in your answer?

I understand that my own health is important and the GMC points this out in their guide Good Medical Practice. I would ensure that I had support from colleagues and work as efficiently as I could to ensure that I reached my appointment on time. Informing the practice manager early in my list of tasks would make it more likely that I was able to leave when I needed to.

Justifying your answer in this way would allow you to place this "other" task much higher on your list of priorities. I am not sure you could justify putting it above the urgent clinical cases (task 3 and 4), but you could easily justify putting it third, fourth or fifth on the list.

Was your ranking appropriate when taking into account the effect on you? If you took account of the effect of task 2 on you or your work by making sure that you attend your appointment, having discussed the situation with the practice manager, you could derive the following ranking:

A 4
B 3
C 2
D 1
E 5
F 6

As you can see, your justification influences your ranking significantly. There is, however, a general order of ranking that must be adhered to.

9 – Reflective learning

Did you leave enough time for the reflective learning?
Did you complete all sections requested?
Did you give the correct number of examples for each section?

Did you learn anything from the exercise?
Were you open to the fact that we all make mistakes?
Did you acknowledge your limitations?
Did you appreciate what you did well?

Is there anything that you would do differently next time after experiencing this exercise?

Did you learn anything about yourself?

Prioritisation 3 | Discussion

Read the brief

Did you spend time reading the brief?

Who are you? Where are you based? What job are you doing?
How much time do you have left on your shift? Who is available to help you?

You know that you are working in General Practice. You know that you are not the only doctor, and have with you the rest of the General Practice team available. The brief mentions a pharmacist, doctor and a receptionist.

There are often other people present in General Practice.
Is there a medical student?
Does the practice have a nurse, counsellor or other allied staff? What about the practice manager?

Who could you use to help with each task?

Message 1
The community Macmillan nurse calls. You have only 15 minutes to resolve this before the pharmacy closes. Can the pharmacist help you? Would they be willing to stay open a little later to help you resolve this issue? Is there a district nurse who could help with the delivery of the prescription and setting up the device? Can the on-call Macmillan nurses help?

Message 2
You are the only person who can complete your application form. If things were quieter, or if the brief was hospital based, you could ask a colleague to cover you while you resolve this issue.

Message 3
Can the partner who certified the death and reported the case to the coroner help? If you were hospital-based, is there a bereavement officer who could talk to the family to explain the process and need for post-mortem.

Message 4
Could the receptionist call the pharmacist for you to explain that you are aware of his call and will respond as soon as you are able? Could the pharmacist come to you? The brief states that they close at 17:00.

Message 5
By justifying this in a way that suggests that the letter has definitely been written, you can ask the practice secretary, receptionist or manager to help with this task.

I always dictate my letters at the end of the surgery that it relates to. I know that the letter will definitely have been dictated and so would ask the practice secretary to check whether it had been typed.

More information

In most of the messages there is little need for additional information.

The assessment criteria

Remember the assessment criteria? (See Figure 10, page 276)

1 – Written skills
If the assessor cannot read your writing, they will be unable to give you the marks that you deserve.

Look at your writing. Can you read it?
Is it clear?
Do you understand what you have written down?
Ask a colleague. Can they read it?

2 – Approach
Did you think about the tasks and messages before you started writing?
Did you make any logical notes?
Are there multiple scribbles on your paper because you changed your mind over and over again?
What could you do differently next time?
If you didn't make notes, try making them during the next practice exercise. You may find that it helps.

If you did make notes, did they help? Did they confuse you? Did you waste precious time making them?

3 – Thought process

Is your thinking and justification clear? Does it make sense?

Is it appropriate? Cross-check your justification with the ranking that you gave them. Do you have multiple mistakes crossed out because you changed your mind?

What would you do differently next time? Is there something you could do to help clarify your thoughts?

Did you try splitting the messages into "patient", "extended patient" and "other"?

"Patient"

Message 1: The community Macmillan nurse calls. A terminal patient of yours needs to start a subcutaneous infusion of morphine. It has been agreed, but you need to write the prescription up and arrange for delivery to the house. The pharmacy closes at 17:00. The Macmillan nurse hands over to an on-call service at 17:00.

"Extended patient"

Message 5: There is a patient in reception who is waiting for a letter that you had promised to leave at reception by Friday afternoon at the latest. The receptionist calls to ask if you can write it now. The patient is agitated.

Message 4: The local pharmacist has called and would like to speak to you about a recent prescription that you have written.

Message 3: The relative of a recently deceased patient has called asking for you to contact them about a request for a post-mortem examination by the coroner. Your colleague had reported the death to the coroner as the patient had died suddenly and had not seen a doctor recently.

"Other"

Message 2.
Your job application for specialist "run through" training is due to be submitted by the end of today. You still have some details to complete before sending it off by email.

Remember that the brief states that you need to leave on time and have the added pressure of your class to think about.

By splitting the messages into these categories it often helps to clarify the general order that the messages should be ranked into.

Note that, depending on the nature of the letter due to the patient in Message 5, this could be considered a direct urgent patient related issue, in which case Message 5 would move up to the "Patient" category alongside Message 1, though with perhaps a lesser priority than Message 1. It will all rest on your justification.

4 – The emergency case

Only the Macmillan request is a true emergency case. The dignity and care of the dying is as important as the care of our living patients.

Did you put the patient first as suggested in the GMC guidance?
Are you a safe doctor?

5 – Ranking

Did you rank the tasks as requested? Did you place the first message in box A and the last message in box E?
How did you fill them in? Did you decide on the obvious last and clear first task and then fill in the other boxes?
Did you fill in the boxes in order?
Whichever way you tried, did it work for you? Is it worth trying the exercise again approaching it in a different way?
Is your ranking appropriate?
Do the "patient-centred" tasks come before the "extended patient" tasks?
Do the "other" tasks rank lower down?

The one exception to this is message 2 – the need for you to spend time on the computer to complete your application process. Did you recognise the effect on you? How did you justify this?

One approach would be to recognise the failing and "mistake" within your answer:

I would usually ensure that anything as important as a job application for run through specialist training was completed well in advance of the

343

deadline. There is no time limit attached to the deadline for application and so I assume that the online application can be submitted before midnight. I could therefore complete this task at home although I realise that it would be on my mind at work. I may need to miss my evening class to complete this task in time.

Depending upon your justification, this "other" task is likely to have ranked last in your list.

Suggested ranking:

A1	This is an obvious first task to complete. The patient is dying and we need to ensure our terminal care and quality of death is as good as it can be.
B 5 C 4	These are both "extended patient" cases and could be placed in any order. Should the pharmacist come first to show our respect for our colleagues? Should the agitated patient's letter come first? This will depend on your justification.
D3	This is an "extended patient" message and, although we have a duty to the relatives of our deceased patients, this is likely to take a significant amount of time to sort out. As such it may be wiser to get tasks 5 and 4 done first.
E 2	Your application form does need to be completed, but can be done in your own time.

6 – Teamwork

Did you use the team?
Did you think about clinical and non-clinical members of the multidisciplinary team?

Was the delegation appropriate?
Should you have completed more tasks yourself?
Should you have completed fewer tasks yourself?

Did you state anywhere that you would check to see if the tasks had been completed and get follow-up from your team members?

7 – Time management

Did you complete the exercise?
Was it much easier with only five tasks to think about?
Did you leave time for the reflective learning?

Are your answers to the first two stems very long with only a sentence for the other stems?
Did you rush the last few stems?

Did you have time to make a clear decision on the ranking or did you feel rushed into it?

How would you allocate the time better if you had to run the exercise again? Is there a better way?

8 – Effect on you

Did you acknowledge that the need to leave on time to attend your evening class would have an effect on you?

There is a box for "other comments" in this question. You could have put in this box (or in the reflective learning part of the exercise) the need to re-evaluate how appropriate it is to have to rush off on a Friday evening to attend a class. This is the last one timetabled until after the summer. Would it be worthwhile trying to rearrange the class for another night of the week?

We need to have an adequate work-life balance and many would argue that we should always be able to leave on-time. If having this deadline to leave would affect your working day due to the added pressure, it may be worth assessing why leaving on-time is so difficult.

Why is it a pressure to leave on-time?
Are there enough doctors in the practice?
Are you being supported enough?
Are you overbooked?
Did you explain this in your answer?

9 – Reflective learning

Did you leave enough time for the reflective learning?
Did you complete all sections requested?
Did you learn anything from the exercise?

Were you open to the fact that we all make mistakes?
Did you acknowledge your limitations?
Did you appreciate what you did well?
Is there anything that you would do differently next time after experiencing this exercise? Did you learn anything about yourself?

Prioritisation 4   Discussion

Read the brief

Did you spend time reading the brief?
Who are you?
Where are you based?
What job are you doing?
How much time do you have left on your shift?

Who is available to help you? You know that you are working in A&E. Remember to use the whole team.

Nurses
Health care assistants
On call doctors from all specialities
Receptionists
Pharmacist
Senior and junior doctors etc…

Who could you use to help with each task?

Task 1
This is an emergency so you need to attend, but you could ask the nurses to insert intravenous access, with severe haematemesis the medical team will need to be called…

Task 2
If the patient died within 24 hours of attending A&E the death will need reporting to the coroner.

Task 3
This patient is stable. Could a nurse call the elderly care team for you? It is unfortunate that she has to wait, but her family are with her.

Task 4
Although this affects you, it is not urgent. You are probably the only person who can complete this task.

Task 5

Is there a nurse practitioner who takes blood gases? Could another A&E doctor help you? Would the surgeon on call help when they attend to review the patient?

More information required

In most of these cases we need to ascertain more information. This should be added to your justification.

Task 1

What are the rest of the observations? Is the blood pressure reading accurate? What else do we know about the patient? Are they on the liver transplant list?

Task 2

Has this patient died within 24 hours of attending hospital? It is likely since you are working in A&E and so would need to be reported to the coroner.

Task 3

The patient is stable but we do not know what they are being admitted with. What are the patient's observations? Is the patient on a suitable mattress if they are bed bound?

Task 4

No further information is required

Task 5

We need to know how stable this patient is. What are their observations? Will they need intensive care? When are the surgeons attending?

The assessment criteria

Remember the assessment criteria? (See Figure 10, page 276)

1 – Written skills

> If the assessor cannot read your writing, they will be unable to give you the marks that you deserve.
> Look at your writing. Can you read it? Is it clear? Do you understand what you have written down? Ask a colleague. Can they read it?

2 – Approach

Did you think about the tasks and messages before you started writing?

Did you make any logical notes?

Are there multiple scribbles on your paper because you changed your mind over and over again?

What could you do differently next time?

If you didn't make notes, try making them during the next practice exercise. You may find that it helps. If you did make notes, did they help?

Did they confuse you? Did you waste precious time writing them?

3 – Thought process

Is your thinking and justification clear?

Does it make sense?

Is it appropriate?

Cross-check your justification with the ranking that you gave them.

Did you cross out multiple mistakes because you changed your mind? What would you do differently next time?

Is there something you could do to help clarify your thoughts?

Did you try splitting the messages into "patient", "extended patient" and "other"?

"Patient"

Task 1, Task 3 & Task 5

"Extended patient"

Task 2

"Other"

Task 4

By splitting the five messages into these categories it often helps to clarify the general order that the messages should be ranked into.

4 – The emergency case

Did you recognise that there were two clinical cases that needed urgent attention: the unstable patient with haematemesis and The patient with pancreatitis.

Did you put the patient first as suggested in the GMC guidance?
Are you a safe doctor?

5 – Ranking

Did you rank the tasks as requested?
Did you place the first task in box A and the last task in box E?
How did you fill them in?
Did you decide on the obvious last and clear first task and then fill in the other boxes?
Did you fill in the boxes in order?
Whichever way you tried, did it work for you? Is it worth trying the exercise again approaching it in a different way?
Is your ranking appropriate?
Do the "patient-centred" tasks come before the "extended patient" tasks?
Do the "other" tasks rank lower down?
In this example there is no real effect on you. Therefore the "other" task should rank last (overdue library fine).

Suggested ranking:

A1	A patient is having severe haematemesis and has collapsed with a blood pressure of 60/40.
B5	You need to take some blood gasses from a patient with pancreatitis. The surgeons are aware of the patient and you are awaiting their review
D3	A stable elderly lady has been in A&E for 3 hours. She needs referral to the elderly care team. Her family keep asking the nurses when she will be moved.
C2	A patient has died and the nurses want you to certify the death.
E4	You need to go to the library to pay a fine on an overdue book.

Remember that there is no absolute answer.

6 – Teamwork
Did you use the team?

Did you think about clinical and non-clinical members of the multidisciplinary team? Was the delegation appropriate?

Should you have completed more tasks yourself?
Should you have completed fewer tasks yourself?

Did you state anywhere that you would check to see if the tasks had been completed and get follow-up from your team members?

7 – Time management
Did you complete the exercise?
Did you leave time for the reflective learning?
Are your answers to the first two stems very long with only a sentence for the other stems?
Did you rush the last few stems?
Did you have time to make a clear decision on the ranking or did you feel rushed into it?
How would you allocate the time better if you had to run the exercise again? Is there a better way?

8 – Effect on you
In this example there was no real effect on you and so the overdue library book should not have affected clinical patient care.

9 – Reflective learning
Did you leave enough time for the reflective learning?
Did you complete all sections requested?
Did you give the correct number of examples for each section?
Did you learn anything from the exercise?
Were you open to the fact that we all make mistakes?
Did you acknowledge your limitations?
Did you appreciate what you did well?

Is there anything that you would do differently next time after experiencing this exercise?

Did you learn anything about yourself?

Prioritisation 5 | Discussion

Read the brief

Did you spend time reading the brief?
Who are you?
Where are you based?
What job are you doing?
How much time do you have left on your shift?

Who is available to help you?

You know that you are working as a surgical on call doctor. You will have a team of doctors around you, nurses, receptionists, ward clerks and possibly even nurse practitioners. Don't forget to use your consultant too if you can!

Who could you use to help with each task?

Task 1
This is an operation that a single surgeon can do. Although it would be easier for you to be there, the registrar could perform this alone. You also have an F1 doctor who could assist or theatre nurses.

Task 2
This is an emergency. You need to attend immediately. A&E is staffed with many doctors and nurses who will stabilise the patient but with your registrar in theatre you could always ask your consultant to come in and help. After all, he's trying to get hold of you anyway.

Task 3
This patient is already in ITU and is being monitored by the team there. You could ask your consultant or your registrar to review this patient when they are available.

Task 4
You need to attend to this task. Use it to your advantage. Ask your consultant to come in to help!

Task 5

This patient could be reviewed by you, any of your team, or you could ask another team doctor to see them prior to discharge if they are available. The patient could always be sent to the discharge lounge to wait for you, if bed space becomes a problem.

More information required

In all cases where messages of this type are left we would always need to ascertain more information. This should be added to your justification.

Task 1

You need to know when the patient will be in theatre. Often, theatre staff call for the doctors to arrive before the patient is sent for. There can often be a long delay whilst the patient is bought to theatre and anaesthetised before you are needed. Ask to be called once the patient is being wheeled into the operating room following anaesthesia.

Task 2

This is an emergency and you need to attend. You could ask for more information regarding their observations, but ultimately you need to go.

Task 3

You could ask for the patient's basic observations and how stable they are.

Task 4

You need no more information. Just call them!

Task 5

You need to know the patient's observations, reason for admission and planned time of discharge. Could they go to the discharge lounge and wait for you?

The assessment criteria

Remember the assessment criteria? (See Figure 10, page 276)

1 – Written skills

If the assessor cannot read your writing, they will be unable to give you the marks that you deserve.

Look at your writing. Can you read it?
Is it clear? Do you understand what you have written down?
Ask a colleague. Can they read it?

2 – Approach

Did you think about the tasks and messages before you started writing?
Did you make any logical notes?
Are there multiple scribbles on your paper because you changed your mind over and over again?
What could you do differently next time?

If you didn't make notes, try making them during the next practice exercise. You may find that it helps. If you did make notes, did they help?

Did they confuse you? Did you waste precious time writing them?

3 – Thought process

Is your thinking and justification clear?
Does it make sense?
Is it appropriate?
Cross-check your justification with the ranking that you gave them.

Did you cross out multiple mistakes because you changed your mind?
What would you do differently next time?

Is there something you could do to help clarify your thoughts?

Did you try splitting the messages into "patient", "extended patient" and "other"?

"Patient"
Task 1, Task 2, Task 3, Task 5

"Extended patient"
No tasks fit into this group

"Other"
Task 4

By splitting the six messages into these categories it often helps to clarify the general order that the messages should be ranked into although in this case, with so many "patient" tasks it doesn't help at all!

4 – The emergency case
Did you recognise the ruptured AAA as the emergency?

Did you put the patient first as suggested in the GMC guidance?
Are you a safe doctor?

5 – Ranking
Did you rank the tasks as requested?

Did you place the first task in box A and the last task in box F?
How did you fill them in?

Did you decide on the obvious last and clear first task and then fill in the other boxes? Did you fill in the boxes in order?

Whichever way you tried, did it work for you? Is it worth trying the exercise again approaching it in a different way?

Is your ranking appropriate?

Suggested ranking:

- A2: You have been asked to attend A&E to review an emergency patient with suspected ruptured AAA (abdominal aortic aneurysm).

- B4: The Consultant on call has left a message for you to contact him. He is unable to reach the Registrar.

- C3: A patient on ITU needs a surgical review for possible small bowel obstruction.

- D1: You need to attend theatre to assist your Registrar with a routine appendectomy.

- E5: A ward patient needs to be reviewed prior to discharge. They are well.

355

Remember that there is no absolute answer.

You must rank the ruptured AAA first. This is an emergency.

The reason for calling the consultant next is that you are going to need help and this is the perfect person to ask. It is a quick task to complete and will help you with the rest of the list. If you didn't put this second, don't worry.

You could put this last as long as you justify it by saying: "Talking to your consultant does not relate directly to patient care and therefore is less important than any other task".

You must however show that you respect the rest of your team too so you could add: "Although my consultant is the head of my team and I respect him, my first duty is to the patients and so I would leave this call till last".

The ward preview is most likely to come last as the patient is stable and awaiting discharge.

You may have ranked the appendicectomy higher. Don't worry. Ensure you justify it appropriately.

6 – Teamwork
Did you use the team?

Did you think about clinical and non-clinical members of the multidisciplinary team? Was the delegation appropriate?

Should you have completed more tasks yourself?

Should you have completed fewer tasks yourself?

Did you state anywhere that you would check to see if the tasks had been completed and get follow-up from your team members?

7 – Time management
Did you complete the exercise?
Did you leave time for the reflective learning?

Are your answers to the first two stems very long with only a sentence for the other stems?
Did you rush the last few stems?

Did you have time to make a clear decision on the ranking or did you feel rushed into it?

How would you allocate the time better if you had to run the exercise again? Is there a better way?

8 – Effect on you
There is no effect on you in this exercise

9 – Reflective learning
Did you leave enough time for the reflective learning?
Did you complete all sections requested?
Did you give the correct number of examples for each section?

Did you learn anything from the exercise?
Were you open to the fact that we all make mistakes?
Did you acknowledge your limitations?
Did you appreciate what you did well?

Is there anything that you would do differently next time after experiencing this exercise?

Did you learn anything about yourself?

Prioritisation 6 — Discussion

Suggested answer: A:2 – B:4 – C:1 – D:5 – E:3 – F:6

Remember there is no "right" answer. Justify your choices appropriately.

The cardiac arrest bleep is your immediate priority. This MUST be placed first.

The asthmatic in A&E sounds as though they are in a critical condition. Talk of HDU means that the patient may be peri-arrest. This requires urgent attention.

The patient on CCU is stable and already in a high dependency area with close monitoring. They need to be seen quickly, but the asthmatic is critically ill and would need stabilising first.

The pharmacy needs to ask about a discharge medication. This is for a planned discharge and the patient is probably waiting. A delay here may prevent another admission.

The self-discharge patient has been deemed stable and fit for discharge from a psychiatric point of view. Most overdoses are not reviewed by psychiatry until they are fit for medical discharge and so this would therefore be last on the list of priorities.

Buying a birthday card from your partner, although important and affects you, could be done on the way home and so is the least important task.

Prioritisation 7 Discussion

Suggested Answer: A:6 – B:1 – C:3 – D:4 – E:5 – F:2

Remember there is no "right" answer. Justify your choices appropriately.

The postpartum haemorrhage is an obstetric emergency and the Registrar is unavailable. This MUST come first. The ectopic in A&E can be stabilised and assessed by the A&E staff until you can attend.

The ruptured ectopic is a gynaecological emergency. The patient is being looked after by A&E staff who can stabilise and resuscitate until you arrive. If you put this first don't worry, as long as you justified it.

The Registrar needs your assistance, but it is possible to do a section with the theatre nurses' assistance. You would obviously attend as soon as you could.

The antenatal patient will need to be seen, but this is not an emergency.

The audit is important and may interfere with your work if you are preoccupied and anxious about finishing it. It should have been finished well in advance of the presentation tomorrow and you will have time at the end of your shift.

Your dental appointment is tomorrow and although it is important to cancel in advance, you could have cancelled earlier. If you scored this higher as it is a quick call, as long as you justified it, it is ok provided you prioritised it lower than the two emergencies.

Prioritisation 8 Discussion

Suggested Answer: A:5 – B:6 – C:4 – D:2 – E:3 – F:1

Remember there is no "right" answer. Justify your choices appropriately.

The patient on the line with chest pain is a clinical emergency. They may be in the middle of an acute myocardial infarction. Assessment of the symptoms over the phone is quick and easy. If there is any doubt they should call 999.

Your mother has called to say your father is in hospital. This could affect you personally and so you may choose to rank this higher than other stable patient care.

The child who is in the surgery and about to have an immunisation is a "patient" task. You need to find out what vaccination they are having as an atopic child (eczema) with an egg allergy could have an anaphylactic reaction.

The health visitor is concerned. If it were a life and death situation then they would contact social services or the police directly, so this is likely to be for advice. This can therefore be classed as an "extended patient" task and be ranked third.

Talking to the practice manager about the on-call rota may be a quick task to complete. The on-call rota impacts on patient care (particularly if the practice manager needed you to cover the on-call that afternoon) and should be completed before a non-patient task.

The teaching of medical students is important and the GMC guidance states that we all have a duty to educate the next generation of doctors. This task was given to you at short notice and it is therefore not your fault that you have a short time frame for preparation. You won't mind doing a favour to whomever asked you to run the session, but this cannot be at the expense of patient care.

Prioritisation 9 | Discussion

Suggested Answer: A:4 – B:2 – C:3 – D:5 – E:1 – F:6

Remember there is no "right" answer. Justify your choices appropriately.

Task 4: This is an emergency and you must attend immediately

Task 2: This is a patient related task and is a quick thing to complete. We should always try to assist our colleagues as quickly as we can.

Task 3: Although this patient is stable, she needs admission and the sooner you review her, the sooner she can be moved to a gynaecological ward.

Task 5: This is a fairly quick task and affects the rest of the O&G team. You could justify this as even higher up if you have a "smart phone". For example: On my way to labour ward to insert the venflon. I would send an email from my "smart phone" to the secretary. This way you could even put this as high as the second task that you complete!

Task 1: This is an extended patient task. You could eat something with your coffee if you are hungry and push lunch back a little further, (or buy your lunch on the way- see below).

Task 6: It is only 13:00 (check the brief at the beginning of the question!). It is still quite early for lunch. You could rank this higher is you said "I would buy myself lunch on the way to meeting my registrar to eat with the coffee.

Prioritisation 10 | Discussion

Suggested Answer: A:3 – B:5 – C:2 – D:4 – E:1

Remember there is no "right" answer. Justify your choices appropriately.

Task 3: The section will not wait for you. You need to attend.

Task 5: Although the child is stable they need admitting as soon as possible. Children with asthma can be unpredictable.

Task 2: Although this is a routine task, mum is waiting on the day unit. You need to attend as soon as you can.

Task 4: It is important to remember your own training and development is important. Your consultant is waiting for you.

Task 1: The registrar can perform the ward round himself but you can join them as soon as your tasks are complete. You may want to rank this higher if you justify it by saying: "I would call my registrar and explain that I am busy and cannot attend the ward round at the earlier time". You can always ask for their help during the call too! This way you could rank it as high as the 2nd or 3rd task to be completed.

Prioritisation 11 Discussion

Suggested Answer: A:1 – B:3 – C:2 – D:6 – E:4 – F:5

Remember there is no "right" answer. Justify your choices appropriately.

Task 1: This is a psychiatric emergency. The patient needs to be seen as soon as possible to admit them and free up the police.

Task 3: This patient should be seen as soon as you can. It is important for all patients (especially psychiatric patients) to have their medication on time.

Task 2: This is a quick task to complete whilst on the ward after admitting the patient in task 3.

Task 6: It is important to have "natural breaks" whilst we work and we should not neglect our own needs. You could rank this higher if you said you would fill in the drug chart whist drinking the coffee!

Task 4: Although this could be done in your own time, the deadline for this job is today.

Task 5: The teaching session is tomorrow. You could complete the presentation after work has finished.

Prioritisation 12 Discussion

Suggested Answer: A:3 – B:2 – C:4 – D:5 – E:1 – F:6

Remember there is no "right" answer. Justify your choices appropriately.

Task 3: This is an emergency. You need to attend immediately.

Task 2: This is an emergency, but the patient is in A&E with a team of A&E staff looking after them. You need to attend as soon as you can after reviewing the ward patient. Remember to ask for help from other members of the team!

Task 4: This could be an urgent call. Don't forget the affect on yourself. If you say "I would call my sister on the way to the car park" (see task below), it allows this to be ranked higher.

Task 5: You need to ensure your car is not clamped or removed. This should not come before urgent patient care, but can be ranked above routine patient care as long as you justify it appropriately.

Task 1: This patient needs to be seen, but is stable and awaiting discharge.

Task 6: The clinic is the least important task. It will be staffed with doctors. Once you are finished you can then attend.

Prioritisation 13 | Discussion

Suggested Answer: A:1 – B: 2 – C: 3 – D:4 – E:5

Remember there is no "right" answer. Justify your choices appropriately.

Tasks 1, 2 and 3: All of these tasks have an equal importance and can be ranked in any order as long as you justify it. You may think it is more important for the relatives of the deceased patient to see you first, you may leave this to the 3rd task to complete if you justify it by wanting to "give the family more time" and you will be less rushed.

Task 4 and 5: These 2 tasks are less important than the patient related tasks and should come after tasks 1, 2 and 3 are completed, but it does not matter whether task 4 or 5 is first.

Prioritisation 14 Discussion

Suggested Answer: A:2 – B:6 – C:5 – D:4 – E:3 – F:1

Remember there is no "right" answer. Justify your choices appropriately.

Task 2: This is your immediate priority

Task 6: If a patient is disturbed, you need to ask for more information and review them as soon as possible. The well-being of the ward staff and other patients may be at risk.

Task 5: This is a quick task and you can complete it whilst on the ward (you can rank this lower down if you justify appropriately).

Task 4: Remember to respect your GPs and not to keep us waiting. We are marking your written paper after all! This is a fairly quick task and could be done "on the way to A&E".

Task 3: This patient needs to be admitted. The sooner they are in ward bed the better

Task 1: You may have ranked this much higher if it is important to you.

Prioritisation 15 | Discussion

Suggested Answer: A:2 – B:3 – C:6 – D:5 – E:1 – F:4

Remember there is no "right" answer. Justify your choices appropriately.

Task 2: This may be an abdominal aortic aneurysm. He needs to be seen as a priority.

Task 3: This is an emergency patient and needs your input, but the A&E team are still with him. This is why he comes after task 2.

Task 6: If this man is dehydrated, he needs IV access and fluids as soon as possible. He will also be in severe pain with SBO.

Task 5: Children need to be seen as a priority, but this child has had pain for a week and he is apyrexial so this is unlikely to be abdominal sepsis. BEWARE: Children often mask serious illnesses as they "compensate". Try to review them as soon as you can.

Task 1: This may be appendicitis.

Task 4: This is a chromic problem and although needs to be assessed and treated as soon as you can, is the most stable case and so can come last

Prioritisation 16 Discussion

Suggested Answer: A:4 – B:1 – C:2 – D:3 – E:5 – F:6

Remember there is no "right" answer. Justify your choices appropriately.

Task 4: This is going to affect you (unless you justify it otherwise). Make a quick call and then move on to the other tasks

Task 1: This is a clinical mistake – admit your mistakes and correct them quickly. This boy needs his antibiotics

Task 2: You do not know why this patient wants a visit. Just because "usually" it is for a repeat prescription does not mean they are not ill now. Make a quick call to the patient "to get more information" and then you can assess when you will attend the visit.

Task 3: The patient has been admitted and so is being looked after by a medical team. We need to respect our colleagues and respond to enquiries as quickly as we can. (You may have ranked this higher as it will be a quick task to complete. Just make sure you justify it appropriately).

Task 5: This will affect you but can wait until the "patient" and "extended patient" tasks have been completed.

Task 6: The F2 has left his number; you can always contact them at the end of the day, or leave this non urgent task for another day.

Prioritisation 17 | Discussion

Suggested Answer: A:1 – B:2 – C:4 – D:3 - E:5 – F:6

Remember there is no "right" answer. Justify your choices appropriately.

Task 1: This patient will be in significant pain and the nurses will be very worried. They need review immediately. An incident form will also need to be completed.

Task 2: This is a quick task and can be completed whilst you are on the ward. The patient has only vomited twice in 12 hours and so this is not an "emergency".

Task 4: This is a quick task and can be completed whilst on the ward.
Note: it does not matter if task 4 comes before task 2. Just ensure you justify it appropriately.

Task 3: It is 15:00pm (look at the brief) and you have not had a drink. It is important that you ensure you have natural breaks during your working day. Do not neglect yourself.

Task 5: This patient has been seen and assessed by A&E. You need to see them as soon as you can but since they are stable it can wait a short time whilst the above tasks are completed. Always add an apology if a patient has been kept waiting:

When I did see this patient, I would apologise for the delay in seeing them.

Task 6: Your GMC fees can be paid on line or over the phone. Although they should be paid on (or before) the annual due date, you are always given a few days "grace" to complete the payment.

Prioritisation 18 | Discussion

Suggested Answer: A:2 – B:6 – C:5 – D:4 – E:1 – F:3

Remember there is no "right" answer. Justify your choices appropriately.

Task 2: This is the equivalent of a crash call in general medicine. You need to attend immediately.

Task 6: An ectopic pregnancy is a gynaecological emergency. You need to see this patient urgently but she is stable currently and with the A&E staff and so can wait until after the "crash" call.

Task 5: This is a "patient" orientated task and needs to be completed as soon as you can. If you have time think about differential diagnoses, e.g. infection (chest, uterine, wound), deep vein thrombosis (DVT).

Task 4: This is an "extended patient" task and although it is important to free up beds, the women could wait in the day room or the discharge lounge (if they are well enough) until you are able to see them. This would to free up the beds if they are needed urgently.

Task 1: This will affect you and needs to be completed BEFORE you drive home today.

Task 3: Rewriting drug charts can take some time and need to be completed as soon as you can.

Prioritisation 19 | Discussion

Suggested Answer: A:3 – B:1 – C:5 – D:4 – E:6 - F:2

Remember there is no "right" answer. Justify your choices appropriately.

Task 3: This is your immediate priority.

Task 1: Subarachnoid haemorrhage could be an emergency and needs immediate review.

Task 5: This is going to affect you (Has someone stolen your credit card details?) and so can be ranked higher than STABLE patient care.

Task 4: This is a quick call. The F2 will be worried about her mother; and in the interests of 'supporting' our colleagues, it is good practice to let her know as soon as you can.

Task 6: Although this patient needs review as soon as you can, they are with the A&E team and have ben stabilised. A COPD patient with saturations of 96% on air is rare and the stem above states that they are "well".

Task 2: This patient needs review but the patient is "stable".

Note: You may have ranked tasks 6 and 2 differently. Don't worry, justify them appropriately. Remember there is no "right" answer.

Prioritisation 20 Discussion

Suggested Answer: A:4 – B:5 – C:1 – D:6 – E:3 – F:2

Remember there is no "right" answer. Justify your choices appropriately.

Task 4: This is your immediate priority.

Task 5: The child needs to be seen as soon as you can.

Task 1: The scalp laceration is stable and not bleeding and so can wait until after the child has been seen.

Task 6: This is a stable "patient" task but can wait until the other cases have been dealt with.

Task 3: You need to collect the notes. In the brief it states that it is 9am and the notes are not needed until lunchtime. Did you realise?

Task 2: This is a clerical task and should wait until, the "patient orientated tasks have been completed.

Note: You may have put tasks 2 and 3 in a different order. Remember there is no right answer. Justify it!

Prioritisation 21 Discussion

Suggested Answer: A:4 – B:6 – C:3 – D:5 – E:1 – F:2

Remember there is no "right" answer. Justify your choices appropriately.

Task 4: This is a diabetic ketoacidosis (DKA) and needs to be seen. They can become very ill very quickly.

Task 6: A palliative care patient needs to be seen quickly. Dignity in death is very important. Even though they are pain free now, you need to ensure they have medication available to prevent their pain returning.

Task 3: This is a diabetic hypoglycaemia. Although the patient is stable it is worth seeing them quickly to ensure they maintain their blood sugar.

Task 5: A suspected DVT is a fairly quick patient to see and review.

Task 1: The saturations are good on this patient and so there is no urgency to see and review them.

Task 2: If this girl has only drank alcohol she needs to sleep it off with rehydration. Once she is not under the influence of alcohol anymore then she can be reviewed from a mental health point of view.

Note: Other than the DKA, it doesn't matter what order the other tasks are put in. Ensure you justify them appropriately.

Prioritisation 22 | Discussion

Suggested Answer: A:3 – B:5 – C:4 – D:1 – E:2 – F:6

Remember there is no "right" answer. Justify your choices appropriately.

Task 3: An asthmatic who is short of breath and unable to talk in sentences is an emergency and needs treatment immediately.

Task 5: A young child who is vomiting and not drinking will get dehydrated very quickly. The child will need to be reviewed. Making a quick telephone call to mum (or asking the receptionist to do it for you) will ensure the child is seen at the surgery as quickly as possible.

Task 4: This child is apyrexial and so there is no concern about meningitis which would otherwise make this task a priority. By reviewing her early in our list of tasks means the nurse is then free to see other patients.

Task 1: The practice manager needs to park. Next time "learn" from your mistake and state "I would ensure I do not park in another person's car parking space again".

Task 2: This will be playing on your mind and only requires a quick call.

Task 6: Repeat prescriptions by definition are not urgent. Most practices have a 48 hour turn around time.

Prioritisation 23 | Discussion

Suggested Answer: A:5 – B:2 – C:4 – D:3 – E:1 – F:6

Remember there is no "right" answer. Justify your choices appropriately.

Task 5: This will affect you and is a very quick call to make to ask someone to check. You could call from your mobile phone whilst walking to the next task.

Task 2: This is potentially an emergency. You need more information and to review the person urgently.

Task 4: This patient is unstable and needs an urgent scan. You have already delayed it by 25 minutes!

Task 3: A vomiting patient is unlikely to proceed to barium enema.

Task 1: Sitting in on interventional procedures is good experience in radiology if you are interested. Once the "patient" tasks are completed, you are then free to observe.

Task 6: Following the interventional procedure you will hopefully have time to review the X-rays before lunch. It is 09:00am, did you realise?

Prioritisation 24 | Discussion

Suggested Answer: A:1 – B:3 – C:2 – D:4 – E:5 – F:6

Remember there is no "right" answer. Justify your choices appropriately.

Task 1: This is your immediate priority

Task 3: This is an emergency. You must attend as soon as the arrest call is over.

Task 2: This patient needs review as soon as you can. They are in pain. You do not know the cause of the collapse.

Task 4: Always try and support your colleagues when you can. This is a quick task and you can also ask the F1 to come to review the GP admissions with you!

Task 5: GP admissions should be reviewed as soon as possible.

Task 6: Although many people are "addicted" to using the internet, we should avoid using it at work for personal use. This can be done in your own time.

Prioritisation 25 Discussion

Suggested Answer: A:4 – B:2 – C:3 – D:5 – E:6 – F:1

Remember there is no "right" answer. Justify your choices appropriately.

Task 4: Coffee is quick to make and you can drink it whilst completing your next task. (You can of course also rank this task last if you prefer, though doing it first may make you work better thereafter!)

Task 2: Although completing blood test request forms is not an emergency, you only have 30 minutes (it is 08:30am and the phlebotomist arrives at 09:00am) to complete them. If you do not fill in the forms, you will have to take the blood and that will take up a lot of your time. This is your priority.

Task 3: This is a quick task and the patient's medication is already overdue by 2 hours.

Task 5: We must respect our colleagues and talking about a difficult patient is important. A plan of action needs to be made to ensure it doesn't happen again tonight.

Task 6: The charts need to be rewritten by 10:00am.

Task 1: The notes need collating by lunchtime.

Prioritisation 26 Discussion

Suggested Answer: A:3 – B:1 – C:5 – D:6 – E:2 – F:4

Remember there is no "right" answer. Justify your choices appropriately.

Task 3: This is a quick call to arrange to see the patient, or you could ask the receptionist to call them for you and get them to come in.

Task 1: It is important to start on time in General Practice. You only have 10 minutes per patient. If you start late, every subsequent patient will have to wait to see you.

Task 5: This is a routine visit and can be done at the end of surgery.

Task 6: This is a routine visit and can be done at the end of surgery.

Task 2: This is an "extended patient" task and should be completed as soon as you can.

Task 4: This does affect you but should not come before patient care.

Prioritisation 27 Discussion

Suggested Answer: A:4 – B:3 – C:5 – D:6 – E:2 – F:1

Remember there is no "right" answer. Justify your choices appropriately.

Task 4: This is an urgent clinical task and needs addressing urgently

Task 3: This is a patient task and needs to be completed before you leave.

Task 5: This is a quick telephone call to make. You will need to advise the patient to make an appointment with another doctor explaining that you are leaving.

Task 6: This is a quick telephone call. The message does not appear urgent, so it is unlikely that you will rank it much higher than this – unless of course you justify it accordingly.

Task 2: This needs completing before you leave, but you should not be late for your leaving party. You can start to clean out the room and then attend the party on time, returning to your room afterwards to complete the clean out.

Prioritisation 28 Discussion

Suggested Answer: A:6 – B:2 – C:3 - D:5 - E:4 - F:1

Remember there is no "right" answer. Justify your choices appropriately.

Task 6: This is an emergency and your first priority.

Task 2: This patient needs admitting and theatre arranging. The sooner they are booked in, the sooner their operation is likely to happen.

Task 3: This is an acute admission but not an emergency. The child should be assessed as soon as you can.

Task 5: The earlier you take blood tests, the earlier the results will be returned from the lab. In post operative patients it does make a difference as you can then decide if any treatment is required before you leave for the day rather than handing over to the on-call staff e.g. blood transfusions.

Task 4: It is important to ensure medication is rewritten to allow the nurses to give the required medication at the correct time.

Task 1: The consultant and registrar are both in theatre. It only takes 2 surgeons to complete a hip replacement, you could therefore miss the start of the procedure.

Prioritisation 29 Discussion

Suggested Answer: A:2 – B:1 – C:3 - D:5 – E:6 – F:4

Remember there is no "right" answer. Justify your choices appropriately.

Task 2: This could be a myocardial infarction (heart attack). This is your first priority.

Task 1: Your car needs moving, you can move it on your way to the home visit (see below).

Task 3: This child may have meningitis and so should be seen as soon as possible.

Task 5: On your way back to the surgery you could make this call. On your hands free kit of course!

Task 6: This is a quick call.

Task 4: The letters are non-urgent.

Prioritisation 30 Discussion

Suggested Answer: A:6 – B:3 – C:2 – D:4 – E:1 – F:5

Remember there is no "right" answer. Justify your choices appropriately.

This is a difficult prioritisation as there are several "serious" cases. Ensure you justify them appropriately. Remember there is no "right" answer.

Task 6: If you need to go to the toilet you will not be able to concentrate or be of much use. Go straight away.

Task 3: The arrest bleep should always be attended immediately. Once you are there, if there are enough doctors you could ask to be relieved to attend the next task.

Task 2: This is an emergency.

Task 4: If the nurses are asking for help, you should support them as soon as possible, The lives of other patients and staff may be at risk from an aggressive patient.

Task 1: This patient although very sick is in A&E with the A&E staff. They will manage the patient until you get there.

Task 5: This patient is in A&E with the staff there and is less serious than the asthmatic.

N Facts you may need to know

This list is endless as in theory any issue from primary or secondary care could be covered in the assessment centre. You will be familiar with most subjects if you have worked in the NHS and are a UK graduate. If you have not worked in the NHS, I would suggest you do some reading about working in the NHS and look at current issues in the medical press.

Any clinical case will be based at the F2 level. You do not need to know everything. The Stage 2 assessment has checked your clinical knowledge. Remember that the stage 3 assessment is more about HOW you do things, rather than WHAT you know. In real life you would admit you don't know and ask for help. This is exactly what you must do in the assessment centre. There are likely to be marks for admitting you do not know something!

The following is a short summary of some key topics of interest. You do not need to know about them in detail. Just ensure you are aware what they mean and be prepared to admit your limited knowledge on the day if they arise.

Admitting mistakes

It is essential to be honest when working as a doctor and to admit our mistakes as soon as they happen. If you discover that you have made a clinical mistake, you MUST report it to a senior member of your team who should then help you to discuss the problem (if appropriate) with the patient concerned. Very often mistakes turn into complaints and then litigation cases because the patient is seeking an explanation and an apology that is never given by the doctor concerned. Sometimes admitting a mistake, talking to a patient and offering a prompt apology means that you can avoid that complaint.

Note: Please always be guided by your senior doctors. Discuss the problem first, before approaching the patient at your level.

Appraisal

Every year during your training as a junior doctor you will (or should) undergo several reviews with your trainers. On an annual basis, you will have a "formal assessment" which will determine whether you will proceed to the next level of speciality training.

Once you are qualified as a GP or a consultant and enter the "specialist register", you are then required to have an annual appraisal. This is a formal review of your year's work allowing you to reflect on your practice and approach to medicine (based on the principles and values in the GMC guidance "Good Medical Practice"), review your current role and set a new professional development plan for the following year.

The annual appraisal is compulsory and in time will become part of revalidation of every doctor.

Asking for help

It is essential for all personnel working within the NHS to know their own limitations and to ask for help when required. Knowing your own strengths and weaknesses plays a part in this. Reflective practice will help you understand what you know and do not know. Never forget to ask for help from your team.

Audit

Audit is an essential part of all NHS work in the UK. It allows us as clinicians to look at our LOCAL practice and to assess how it compares to a set standard. We can then monitor our work ensuring best possible care.

It is based on the "audit cycle"

1. Identify a subject
2. Decide on what criteria you wish to monitor
3. Set the "gold standard". (Achieving 100% is unlikely. Ensure standards set are realistic)
4. Plan and then execute the monitoring process

5. Identify any changes that are needed
6. Implement change and plan the re-audit date
7. Re-audit to complete the cycle and monitor the changes made to determine if you have reached your "gold standard".

Note: some people call it the "audit spiral" as the process never ends. The cycle goes on and on.

Pros of audit:
- Improved patient care
- Continued teaching and learning
- A way of ensuring openness and accountability for our current practice.

Cons of audit:
- Time consuming
- Essential part of training and the quality of audits performed can be poor due to the forced nature of the task

Breaking bad news

In all specialities of medicine we have to break bad news. There are no "rules" but there are several things you should think of:

1. **Prepare yourself**
   a. Ensure you have enough time
   b. Ensure you will not be interrupted
   c. Ensure you are ready for a potentially long meeting. Have you been to the toilet? Have you eaten?
   d. Enter the room in the right frame of mind. It is inappropriate to walk into a room where you are about to tell someone they have an incurable disease smiling and being 'jolly'.
   e. Make sure you are about to see the right person. Do not make a mistake; check the notes against the patient/relatives name.

2. **Prepare the room**
   a. Are there tissues?
   b. Is there a 'do not disturb sign' you can use?
   c. Are there enough chairs?

3. **Ensure you have help**
    a. Is there a nurse available to come in the consultation with you?
    b. Is there someone to make tea?

4. **Prepare the patient/ relative**
    a. Do they have someone with them for support?
    b. Would they like you to call anyone?
    c. Ensure they are sitting down.

5. **Break the news as soon as possible using appropriate words.**
    a. If the patient has cancer, say "cancer".
    b. If someone has died, say they are dead.

6. **Show empathy and sensitivity, use phrases such as**
    a. "I am sorry........"
    b. "This must be a shock......"

7. **Reflect back to the patient their emotions**
    a. You look shocked.......
    b. I can see you are upset.......

8. **Use SILENCE.**

9. **Observe their body language/ non verbal communication.**

10. **Check their understanding and offer follow up.**

Caldicott

Guidelines were issued regarding the use of personal identifiable patient information within the NHS. These are called the Caldicott principles and include:

- Do not use identifiable patient information unless absolutely necessary
- Justify the purpose for using patient information
- Use the minimum necessary information possible
- Access to patient information should be on a "need to know " basis only

- Anyone who has access to patient information should be aware of their responsibilities
- Understand and comply with the law

Capacity

For a patient to make an informed decision about their treatment, they must have capacity. It is assumed someone has capacity unless proven otherwise.

Based on the Mental Capacity Act 2005, any health professional may assess capacity, but where there is doubt, it may be helpful to refer to a psychiatrist.

For a patient to have capacity they must be able to:

- Understand the information relating to their condition/ treatment including the pros and cons of both having treatment and not having treatment.
- Retain that information.
- Weigh up the pro's and con's to help make an informed decision.
- Communicate their decision.

If a person has capacity, it is their right to choose.

Child protection

Child protection or 'safeguarding' is an essential part of every doctors working life. You must always have a high index of suspicion when working with children and families. If you ever suspect there is an element of abuse (physical, emotional, sexual abuse or neglect) you must first ensure the safety of the child and then inform a senior member of the team. If you are ever in doubt you can talk to the paediatricians, social services, named GP for child protection, or the police.

Always ensure clear and accurate documentation and follow up any telephone referrals with a written referral.

Clinical governance

Clinical governance is a "framework" based on 7 criteria/pillars, that allows NHS organisations to ensure accountability and continued improvements in clinical care.

The 7 criteria are:

- Teaching and training,
- Information technology
- Clinical care
- Audit
- Risk management
- Staffing
- Patient involvement

Complaints

Every NHS organisation has a complaints procedure that they must follow. Often a complaint can be defused by simply talking to patients and explaining what happened and why.

- All complaints should be dealt with at a local level (GP practice or hospital trust) in the first instance.
- The complaint must be acknowledged (usually within 48 hours of its receipt).
- The complaint should then be fully investigated.
- A written report including outcomes and suggested improvement to care should be completed and the complainant informed. (Usually within 4 weeks).
- If the complainant is not satisfied they are then able request a review (Primary care trust, NHS ombudsman, GMC).

All NHS trusts have a Patient advice and liaison service (PALS) that are independent and act on behalf of the patient. You should always offer this as a means of support to patients who wish to complain.

Confidentiality

It is our responsibility as doctors to respect the confidentiality of our patients. This includes competent minors under 16 but with Gillick competence).

There are rare circumstances where we can breech patient confidentiality. These include:

- Where the public is in danger. (e.g. a patient discloses that they are going to kill someone).
- Where the patient is in danger (e.g. Child abuse)
- Reporting.
    - Illnesses- Public health outbreaks e.g. Measles, salmonella.
    - Adverse drug reactions
- For criminal purposes (e.g. police, court etc.)
- DVLA (if a patient refuses to stop driving on medical advice)

It is always better to inform the patient that you are going to breech their confidentiality before doing so if at all possible. This way you stand a better chance of maintaining your doctor patient relationship in the long term.

Consent

As long as a patient over the age of 16 has "capacity" they are able to consent to treatment. Consent can be implied (the patient holds their arm out for the injection to be given), verbal (the patient says "yes") or written (the patient signs a form).

Always ensure you have clear documentation regarding consent.

Consent and the Fraser ruling

The legal age of consent is 16. In England and Wales, if a minor (under 16-year-old) has "capacity" (see above for the definition) then they can be deemed "Gillick competent" and are able to agree to treatment. This usually applies to teenagers rather than younger children and was initially implemented over prescribing the oral contraceptive pill.

Notes:
1. Children under 16 cannot refuse treatment using "Gillick competence". If a minor is refusing treatment, the parent/guardian or the courts are able to intervene.

2. In Scotland a similar approach applies, except that children who are competent can also refuse treatment.

Crying/ angry patient

During your career you will meet patients who are upset and patients who are angry. It is important for us to recognise these emotions in our patients and allow them in the consultation.

The principles of dealing with these extreme emotions are detailed in the role plays but in general:

Angry patient:
*   Ensure the patient is sitting down.
*   Do not engage with a conversation until the patient sits down
*   Reflect their anger back at them. "I can see you are really angry....."
*   Apologise. "I am sorry you are so angry..."
*   Use silence
*   Ensure you remain calm, do not raise your voice
*   Ensure you maintain eye contact, but do not stare at the patient
*   Ask the patient to stop shouting and to talk to you. "Please stop shouting at me........"
*   Repeat the same phrase in a low tone until the patient calms down. "Please sit down and talk to me... It's really difficult for me to explain while you're shouting at me........"

Note: You must always ensure your own safety first and so if you ever feel threatened in a consultation and the patient will not leave the room, you should leave, or call for help (panic button, emergency bell etc).

Upset/crying patient:
*   Allow the patient to cry
*   Use silence
*   Use touch (if appropriate) e.g. Hand on their hand or arm.

- Offer tissues
- Allow the patient as much time as they need
- Reflect their emotion back to them. "I can see you are really upset..."
- Apologise. "I am so sorry..."
- Mirror the patient's emotion, use a soft, gentle voice and talk at a slower speed than usual.
- Ask if they want someone to support them e.g. relative, chaplain, nurse.

Dangerous colleague – drugs/alcohol/clinical care

Following the GMC guidance "Good medical practice", our patients are always our first concern and we must ensure their safety.

If you suspect a colleague is intoxicated by drugs or alcohol, or is "dangerous" you must first ensure that their patients are safe and if necessary prevent the healthcare professional in question from working.

Once the patients are safe, you must then act to help the doctor concerned by either approaching them yourself, or by involving a senior member of your team. Remember there is a high incidence of depression and addiction in healthcare professionals. They will need support and may need to seek help from their own GP or an appropriate professional organisation.

The accusations must be fully investigated and the healthcare professional may be suspended or sent on "compassionate leave" during the investigation.

Ethical framework

Autonomy: It is the patients right to choose
                   (assuming they have capacity)
Beneficence: First do good
Non maleficence : Do no harm
Justice: Everyone has equal rights, we should not judge
                   based on age, sex, education etc.

Evidence based medicine

Traditionally, doctors practised based on their own personal experience. Today, we use the best available evidence to influence our practice. It is essential that we keep up to date and are able to interpret new evidence and data correctly.

For example: Reading the up to date current NIICE guidelines (SIGN guidelines in Scottland) to influence our management of specific diseases.

GPs with specialist interests (GPwSI)

Many GP's these days (in addition to the day-to-day clinical management of patients), have a specialist interest. This may include any speciality within medicine. For example: Minor surgery, drug rehabilitation, dermatology, acupuncture. They receive referrals from other GP's and decide on treatment with the support of the secondary care consultants. The clinics are usually run within General Practice for the primary care trust and the GP's have undergone specific training to gain "GPwSI" status.

Good medical practice – GMC

This guidance was published by the GMC in 2006 and encompasses the following:

- Good clinical care
- Maintaining good medical practice
- Teaching and training
- Relationships with patients
- Working with colleagues
- Probity
- Health

GMS, PMS practices within the NHS

There are 2 main types of GP practices. They are GMS and PMS practices. This is the type of contract that the GP surgery has with the primary care trust.

The contract determines how the practice is paid for the services it provides and the services that the practice must provide. In the future it is envisaged that the government will alter the contracts to have one general GP contract.

GMS:
This is a nationally agreed contract and in general this includes:

- General medical services (Essential) e.g. general patient care, minor illnesses, chronic diseases and terminal care
- Additional services (Practices may opt out) e.g. contraception, immunisation, child health surveillance, maternity services
- Out of hours provision (Practices may opt out)
- Quality and Outcomes Framework (QuOF)

In addition (for additional money), there are enhanced services that each primary care trust organises to meet the demands of their local population.

PMS:
This is a locally agreed contract allowing the GP's to meet the demands of the local community by shaping the services that they provide to meet the need.

The payments are similar, but have different names. For example:
- "Core services" (general patient care, minor illnesses, chronic diseases and terminal care) and
- "Additional services" Contraception, immunisation, child health surveillance, maternity services

Note: There are alternative GP practices under APMS (Alternative provider of medical services) contracts.

Note: Under the new changes to the NHS, the primary care trust will be replaced by a "cluster" or consortium of GPs.

Incident reporting

If a mistake or problem arises within a healthcare environment it must be reported and investigated. One way to initiate this investigation is by using "incident" reports. This is much more common in hospital practice than in primary care which tend to use "significant event analysis". The incident report should be filled in immediately and submitted to your line manager as soon as possible. The line manager will then look at the incident and investigate it as required.

Multidisciplinary team

In all aspects of medicine we work within a multidisciplinary team and all members of that team are as important as each other. The team in General Practice includes:

Receptionists
Cleaners
Caretakers
Clerical staff
Nurses
Health care assistants
Nursing students
Junior doctors (F1, F2, GPST 1, 2, 3)
Medical students
Midwife
Speech therapist
Pharmacist
Health visitor
Bereavement officer
PALS
Patient and their representatives
GP's
Hospital staff
Practice manager
Occupational health
Physiotherapist
Social worker
Counsellor
Drug advisor, etc.

Nurse practitioners

A nurse practitioner is a qualified nurse who has undertaken additional training (often at degree level) and are able to work in specialist areas.

- There are many nurse practitioners within General Practice that are able to see patients with minor illnesses, triage them, assess their illness and prescribe. Only if they have a problem do they then involve the GP.

- Other nurse practitioners may run diabetic clinics and chronic disease clinics. Offering assessment, care and medicine review/ update to the patients under their care.

Out of hours cover in General Practice

General Practice opening time is usually from 08:00am to 18:30pm. Outside of these hours there is a requirement to provide "out of hours care". There is a provision within the GP contract for this, but the majority of practices "opt out" of covering the out of hours care and loose some of their income accordingly. The Primary care trust then commissions organisations to cover the hours providing care for all patients registered within the area. Many GPs do weekend and evening shifts as a way of increasing their income.

Our own health/ the effect on us

In the GMC's *Good Medical Practice* it states:

You should be registered with a GP outside of your family to ensure you have access to independent and objective medical care. You should not treat yourself".

There is a high incidence of illness, depression and addiction amongst doctors and we should be vigilant not only regarding our own health, but also regarding the health of our colleagues.

Never underestimate the effect of your job on yourself. The difficult diagnoses, the patient death, the long working hours all affect the way we think and feel. You must always allow time for reflection and ask for help when needed.

Practice-based commissioning

Traditionally, the primary care trust decides and "commissions" organisations to provide care for the local population. Practice based commissioning, is where practices (usually a group of local practices), take on the responsibility of holding a budget and "commissioning" (choosing, instructing and paying) organisations to provide care for their local population.

For example: Ultrasound services could be "bought" (by the group of practices) from the local hospital or a private provider who is in the locality. The choice of provider will be determined by quality of service, geography and price.

The government is keen for an increase in practice based commissioning as a way of increasing competition within the NHS in the hope that it will improve standards (quality) whilst driving down costs.

Primary health care team

The primary health care team is the "multidisciplinary team that works within General Practice). See multidisciplinary team.

Probity

This is one of the domains of the GMC's *Good medical practice* guidance. In simple terms it means being honest and trustworthy whist acting with integrity. This involves all aspects of your medical role including your clinical work, research, financial dealings and anything that you write (e.g. CV or reference letter) or publish.

Psychosocial component to the consultation

Every one that you talk to (patients, relatives, colleagues and friends) has a personal life. Their personal like will affect how they think, behave and react. By thinking about the psychosocial influences when dealing with people will ensure that you begin to fully understand the person in front of you. Psychosocial influences include psychological, financial, social, and spiritual influences.

Quality and Outcomes Framework in General Practice (QuOF)

The quality and outcomes framework is a points based system that determines a large amount of how much GMS GP practices get paid each year. (PMS and APMS have similar systems for payment). The higher the points that you score, the higher the income for the practice. The points are based in 4 areas:

- Clinical care
- Organisational
    - Education and training,
    - Records,
    - Practice management,
    - Information for patients,
    - Medicine management.

- Patient experiences
    - Length of consultations
    - Access to GPs

- Additional services
    - Contraception
    - Child health surveillance
    - Maternity
    - Cervical screening

The main aim of QuOF is to improve patient care.

Reflective learning

Reflective learning is not a complex concept. It is a way of looking at the way in which you work, appraising how you work, what is good, what can be improved and what could be done differently next time to improve things further. It can in fact be applied to any exercise or task completed and is often done subconsciously by many people.

A common situation in medical practice where reflective learning is practised is following an arrest call. Image that you were part of an arrest team where the patient sadly died. Rather than returning to A&E to see the next patient on our list, we often spend a little time thinking about what happened, what went well, what could have been done differently, what we found difficult and how we felt about the arrest call. This is reflective thinking. If we use some of that thinking to alter and improve our practice next time, then we have learnt from our experience. This is reflective learning.

Revalidation

Revalidation was introduced as a concept in medicine following the Shipman Inquiry. It has yet to be implemented into clinical practice but will be the way (from approximately 2013) in which all clinicians can prove to the GMC that they are up to date and fit to practice. (www.gmc-uk.org).
Currently to work as a doctor in the UK you need a license to practice, this will be renewed each year by the GMC and this, in addition to your annual appraisal will form part of revalidation. All specialities will have slightly different processes of revalidation, but the principles are the same.

Risk management

Risk management is the process where by all NHS trusts have protocols in place to ensure risks to patients and staff are minimised, monitored and (if things go wrong), investigated fully ensuring we learn from our mistakes.

Note: this is part of clinical governance

Significant event analysis (SEA)

SEA is a means by which a "significant" occurrence in day to day clinical practice can be assessed, investigated and reviewed to see what was good about the practice, what went wrong (if anything), and what we can learn from the event.

Although SEA can be used for excellent clinical care, it usually occurs when mistakes have been made as a means of investigating the occurrence to see why something went wrong and to look at ways of changing practice to ensure the same mistake does not happen again. It is meant as a learning tool not as a way of judging performance.

The white paper. "Liberating the NHS". July 2010

This is the latest white paper released from the government on the future of the NHS. Key points include:

- Giving patients greater choice and control

    - Increased patient control of health records
    - Increased information given to patients
    - Increased choice for patients (choice of GP with open lists to all, choice of hospital, choice of diagnostic tests and treatment etc)
    - Healthwatch England to be created. This will act as the patient's champion.

- Using clinical outcomes rather than "targets" and ensuring "quality of care"

    - Evidence based measures and targets
    - NICE will develop 150 quality standards
    - Quality will be financially rewarded

- Utilising the clinicians "on the ground" providing day to day clinical care to show leadership with decisions being made with a "bottom up" approach rather than the traditional "top down" approach.

- Creating GP consortia following the dissolution of primary care trusts who will control approximately 80% of the NHS budget and work using "practice based commissioning"
- NHS commissioning board will oversee the commissioning process
- All NHS trusts to become foundation trusts and be freed from their current constraints
- Care quality commission to monitor the quality of healthcare
- Monitor to oversee access, competition and regulate the costs of treatment within the NHS

O Summary of proposed assessment criteria

Role play/ Patient simulation

Summary of proposed detailed assessment criteria for role play

1. Creating a safe environment
2. Introduction and putting the patient at ease
3. Active listening and encouragement
4. Relevant psychosocial information
5. Expectations of the patient including any hidden agenda
6. Clinical questioning
7. Explanation and differential diagnosis
8. Working diagnosis and management plan
9. Patient choice
10. Checking the patient's understanding
11. Follow-up and review as required
12. Actor patient's general impression
13. Body language and physical interaction
14. Remaining calm under pressure

Simplified assessment criteria for role play (Use this on the day)

1. **Create a safe environment and read the doctor's brief given to you**
   a. Read, read and read again!
   b. Move the furniture if you need to and put your watch where you can see it

2. **Introduction and active listening**
   a. Start the conversation sensibly
   b. What is the actors expectation?
   c. Are you listening, looking and feeling the emotions?

3. **Verbal communication**
    a. Explanations of diagnoses and plans of action should be clear and pitched at the correct level
    b. Clinical questioning (if appropriate) should show safe practice
    c. Have you given the actor choice?

4. **Non verbal communication**
    a. Your body language (did you remain calm?)
    b. Did you pick up on the actor's body language?
    c. Was there a hidden agenda?

5. **Psychosocial influences**
    Psychological, social, financial, spiritual

6. **Checking understanding and close**
    a. Did you specifically ask if the actor understood?
    b. Is there a follow up or next meeting planned?
    c. Did you finish in 10 minutes?

Prioritisation/ written exercise

1. Written skills
2. Approach
3. Thought process
4. The emergency case
5. Ranking
    -   Patient
    -   Extended Patient
    -   Others
6. Teamwork
7. Time management
8. Effect on you
9. Reflective learning

P References

The following publications and references are mentioned in the text and may be of interest for your preparation.

1. **Caldicott guidelines**
   www.dh.gov.uk

2. **Citizens Advice Bureau**
   www.citizensadvice.org.uk

3. **Cruse Bereavement Care**
   www.crusebereavementcare.org.uk

4. **Department of health (Liberating the NHS)**
   www.dh.gov.uk

5. **Foundation competencies**
   www.foundationprogramme.nhs.uk

6. **General Medical Council**
   www.gmc-uk.org

7. *Good Medical Practice* **(2006). GMC publications**
   www.gmc-uk.org/guidance/good_medical_practice.asp

8. **National Recruitment Office for General Practice Training**
   www.gprecruitment.org.uk

9. **Quality and outcomes framework.**
   www.qof.ic.nhs.uk

10. **Relate counselling**
    www.relate.org.uk

11. **Royal College of General Practitioners**
    www.rcgp.org.uk

OTHER BOOKS IN THIS SERIES

GPST STAGE 2 – Clinical Problem Solving
300 MCQs (Single Best Answer) for GPST / GPVTS entry
4th edition: ISBN 978-1-905812-20-2
Nishali Patel, David Phillips

GPST STAGE 2 – Clinical Problem Solving
1400 EMQs for GPST / GPVTS entry
4th edition: ISBN 978-1-905812-21-9
Nishali Patel, Lisa Hamzah, Ruth Reed, David Phillips

GPST STAGE 2 – Professional Dilemmas
100 scenarios for GPST / GPVTS entry
4th edition: ISBN 978-1-905812-22-6
Olivier Picard, Gail Allsopp